MORE JOY...

An Advanced Guide to Solo Sex

by Harold Litten

Illustrations by Rod Jenson Shows

FACTOR PRESS
P.O. Box 8888
Mobile, Alabama 36689

ISBN   0-9626531-8-7

Library of Congress Cataloging-in-Publication Data:

Litten, Harold, 1940-
More Joy...An Advanced Guide
to Solo Sex/Harold Litten.
200p.; 22 cm.

ISBN 0-9626531-8-7

1. Masturbation. 2. Sex instruction for men. I. Title

CONTENTS

I dedicate this book to Don and Danny and Barry and Bill and John and Russel and Steve and Dick and Robert and Peter and Doug and BeanDip and William and Todd and Hugh and all the many others who have made me feel loved and needed, and with whom I've shared joy over great distances.

Introduction

"I can't put into words the influence your book has had on me. I finished the first two chapters Monday night. Then I closed the book and had an hour of the best solo sex of my life. It was the best for two reasons. First, it was the first time since I was twelve years old and began solo sex that I felt no shame. And second, because I felt no shame, I spent an hour at it instead of three minutes. I am seventy-two years old. Thank you from my heart."

"My friend Jack, twenty-five years, loaned me your book. He said I had dumm [sic] about jerking off being bad. I think different now. Thank you Harold. I will give your book to my kids when I get them my boy kids. I am sixteen almost."

During the past twenty years, I've written more than six hundred articles for scores of publications, some of them with circulations approaching twenty million. I've written twelve books, most of them published by major New York companies. And, like all writers, I've received letters. But nothing in all that experience prepared me for what's occurred since 1990, when the first edition of *The Joy of Solo Sex* was born.

It wasn't just the volume—hundreds upon hundreds of letters from men of all ages. (One father returned a copy saying that it had been purchased by his fourteen-year-old son; he didn't object to his boy's learning how to enjoy solo sex more, but to the fact that the child had stolen the money from his mother to buy it.) What touched me most deeply was the raw honesty of the letters, the shedding of facades, the laying bare, the vulnerability.

These writers used such words as *salvation* from shame, *healing*, the experience of feeling like a *complete* human being again. A minister wrote that he'd always assumed that he had to choose between God and the pleasures of his body, and that now, for the first time in two decades, he realized that he could embrace God and his cock at the same time, that the orgasm was a sacrament, a means of worship.

Married women wrote to say that they had learned through the book new ways to please their husbands. Couples told me about their newly found pleasures in solosex sharing.

Some of these letters were rather potent. (The following has been edited for proper usage and punctuation.) For example:

> Your book was hot and I learned a lot from it, but you didn't say much about group solo sex. After my girlfriend and I read your book, we had an experience that you might be able to use sometime.

> Carol is twenty-three, with long brown hair, nice shape, and a nurse, which is good because she looks great in white. I am twenty-five and pretty muscular, which comes from being in construction work. My best friend, Rick, is Carol's age. We work together, but Rick does trim, and he's kind of skinny.

We asked Rick to come over for drinks one Friday night. We got hot just thinking about it. When the door bell rang, I ran into the shower. Carol let him in, hugged him, led him to the sofa. On the table was our copy of *The Joy of Solo Sex*.

"Joe left that for you to borrow," she told him. He picked it up and looked it over while Carol went to get him a drink.

A few minutes later I came out of the shower naked, a towel over my shoulder, and sat at the opposite end of the sofa from Rick. He must have rearranged himself when he was alone in the room because, instead of his dick pushing down on his leg, it was actually pushing up behind his belt. You could easily see the shape of the head under his T-shirt.

Carol came in, put the three drinks on the table, and sat between us. She glanced at the page Rick was studying.

"Oh, that's Tug the Testes—Joe really likes that one," she told Rick. "Want to see how it works?" I saw Rick's Adam's apple move up and down when he swallowed.

"Well, sure," he said.

"Stand up," she told me. I did, facing Rick. My dick started to swell, because I guess I'm an exhibitionist, and this was really hot.

Carol stood behind me and reached between my legs to take my balls in her hand. She began tugging gently, making my dick flop around until it started jutting straight out. I kept my eyes focused on Rick's but he was staring at my cock and Carol's hand.

Finally, Carol stopped. "Come on, you should try it, too," she told Rick. "Stand up." I could see the

9

embarrassment in his face. We'd never done anything even mildly sexy together before. Still, almost like a man hypnotized, he got to his feet.

Carol lifted his shirt over his head. She unbuckled his pants, pulled down his zipper, tugged his undershorts to below his knees.

"Wow!" she said. His dick pointed straight toward the ceiling.

Carol moved behind him. "Now, spread," she said, reaching between his legs. She grabbed his balls and began tugging just as she had done with mine.

I reached behind me to take my own balls in my hand, and matched Carol's rhythmic tug on Rick. I could see the heat rising in his chest and neck and face as we both got higher and higher. Without being shy, we studied each other's bodies, looked straight into each other's eyes.

Rick came first, his knees bending, the muscles of his torso spasming, his head thrown back, eyes closed, mouth opened. The first shot landed on my leg, and that sent me over the edge. The carpet was a mess.

Afterward, we both petted Carol off. The three of us have been together about five times now. We always do just solo sex together, and Rick and I have played with each other while Carol watched. But we won't ever get together just the two of us guys. We need Carol to make sure what we're doing isn't gay.

Many letters were like this one, suggesting many facets of solosexuality that I hadn't discussed in the first book. Although *The Joy of Solo Sex* remains far and away the most detailed guide ever published on the subject, it was never intended to be exhaustive. It was an introduction to advanced solosexual pleasure.

A few months after publishing that book, I knew that I would eventually write *More Joy....* For one thing, readers had virtually demanded that we publish *CELEBRATE The Self* Newsletter, a forum in which like-minded men share techniques and experiences. Through the newsletter, I learned of many new toys and techniques, and corresponded with many readers to obtain details. Some of these stories are in print for the first time in these pages.

In some ways, *More Joy...* exemplifies certain parts of the first book. Readers have shown us, for example, how to make a great many new, pleasurable solosex devices at little or no cost. We've corresponded with men who practice autoerotic games for days without interruption except to eat and sleep. More is going on out there in Your Town, USA, than anyone can possibly imagine.

But this book also goes well beyond the first. I will show you how to breathe orgasmically, how to play solosex games with others and reach highs that may be the best shared sex you've ever had. I'll discuss "Brinkmanship," a popular game among solosexuals.

But the most important information I'll be sharing with you, in my mind, will probably prove to be the most controversial as well. That's because it goes beyond the physical, the tangible, reaches into what has inadequately been dubbed "the spiritual."

If you've already made up your mind concerning this sort of thing and have shut the door firmly and turned the lock, then the last chapter of this book, although anecdotally entertaining, will not be of much help to you personally. I recommend that you skip it. You will already have gotten more than your

11

money's worth. As for me, although I am a skeptic by nature, professionally committed to demanding the empirical evidence and nothing more, I have reached this conclusion: When the body and that which is within the body but is not flesh are united in Eros something so far beyond words can happen that it is otherworldly

The incredible truth is that even some of our most revered saints experienced this unity of flesh, spirit, and Eros and, in their naive integrity, described precisely what they felt. Saint Bernard, writing from experience, said, "If anyone once receives the spiritual kiss of Christ's mouth he seeks eagerly to have it again and again." He wrote of being "intoxicated with love."

Hadewijach of Antwerp, a "bridal mystic" living in the mid-thirteenth century, wrote:

> Calm reigns at last
> When the loved one received from her Beloved
> The kisses that truly pertain to love.
> When he takes possession of the loved soul in every way,
> Love drinks in these kisses and takes them to the end.
> As soon as Love thus touches the soul,
> She eats its flesh and drinks its blood.
> Love that thus dissolves the loved soul
> Sweetly leads them both to the invisible kiss—
> That same kiss which reunites
> The Three Persons in one sole being.

The ecstasies detailed by Saint Teresa and Saint John of the Cross are frankly erotic, and strongly suggest that their erotic experiences were orgasmic. They were no doubt psychic orgasms, induced not by physical stimulation but by an altered state of consciousness in which the spiritual and the sexual became synonymous.

Others—many others—had similar experiences, and I'll share them with you in later chapters. But the thing to keep in mind now is that these passionate pillars of the Christian Church had divided their beings, through ghastly, irrational theology, into two artificial parts—the body, which was evil, and the spirit, which was holy. In practice, they condemned the flesh. Saint Teresa dressed and slept in cloth so rough it chaffed her skin, and Saint John flagellated himself and cut his body with shards of glass.

But erotic passion—lust—cannot be abolished. This is the rather stupid illusion held by those who advocate sexual abstinence among teenagers. Sexual hunger will be satisfied, whether through normal channels or hideous perversion.

In the case of the saints, worship became an erotic act so intense as to lead to orgasm. Both John and Teresa so intensely imagined physical union with the body of Jesus, and both had such vivid imaginations and deep longing for Eros, that orgasm was inevitable.

Since about the sixth century AD, the Church has defined the body and its sexuality as evil—or, at best, to be endured. Skeptics, on the other hand, have gone to the opposite extreme, denying those aspects of reality that can't be squeezed into a test tube. Neither view represents a unified, complete individual. For such an individual, the sex experience is perhaps half what it could be. We will learn how to put ourselves back together in these pages, and how to experience the full celebration of the Bodyspirit.

But let's begin by retracing when and where it all began...

PART ONE

Solosexuality—Loving Yourself All The Way

Chapter One

The Joy of Solo Sex

Since *The Joy of Solo Sex* was first published in 1990, I've been asked just short of a million times, "What on earth ever led you to write a book on such a subject?" (Presumably it would have been more socially acceptable to publish something like, *Twenty-Five Proven Ways to Bake, Broil, and Preserve Your Parents—Murder Made Easy.*

The truth is, apart from my quarter of a century as a health and medical writer, I am an *expert* in solo sex. The only thing I've done more than jerk off is *breathe*! And now, thanks to articles, lectures and the book, I am truly an internationally recognized expert on masturbation. Or, as one of my readers put it, "You are the world's leading apostle of autoeroticism."

As such, let me stifle some myths at the outset: it is true that I have had cataracts removed from both eyes. I've had a detached retina reattached in the left eye. I've had yag laser something-or-other done to remove moisture from both eyes. And I wear glasses.

But I have not gone blind.

Nor do I have warts in the palms of my hands. And I am not insane. (Although both my wife and my friend Dave occasionally question that).

But the real reason I wrote *The Joy of Solo Sex* and continue with this volume is that I am sick to death of sexual shame. At birth, millions of children are nailed into a coffin of conscience created by the church and their parents. They live in it and eventually they die in it—the whole thing is a preposterous lie. Whatever I can do to set those people free I will do, even if it takes the rest of my energy and all of my life.

It began for me in Mr. Coons' Sunday school class. Mr. Coons was a Baptist who told us twelve-year-olds, "You are all sinners, every one of you."

I didn't feel like a sinner, and I didn't remember doing any sins, so I asked, "Mr. Coons, what sins do I do?"

His face reddened. "You know, you evil little boy. And God knows. He sees those dark, nasty things you do late at night in your room when the lights are out."

My blood temperature must have hit 110. I felt its heat in my face. So I went home and vowed that I would never, ever touch my penis again.

By Tuesday night I broke my vow. It felt great, but my soul grew tortured. The following Sunday I met with Mr. Coons after Sunday school class.

"You know, Mr. Coons...that sin you were talking about last week, at night, alone."

"Yes, son. Here, come sit on my knee and tell me all about it."

I did, while he fondled my butt.

"Well, I do it."

"You do what? Tell me the details."

"Well, I play with it."

"And it gets hard, right?"

I nodded. Mr. Coons began breathing rapidly. "It gets big and feels real good, right?"

"Yes."

"So good. Ah, so good. So goood." His eyes widened, his face flushed. He squeezed my butt till it hurt. Then, suddenly, he pushed me off his lap.

"Well you mustn't do it any more," he scolded. "It's a sin, a terrible sin. You must stop!"

"But that's why I'm here, Mr. Coons. How can I stop? I try. What can I do?"

He cleared his throat, straightened his tie, brushed the damp protrusion in his trousers. "You must think of Jesus, boy," he said. "Think of Jesus dying on the cross, hanging there for your sins."

So I tried. Every time I felt the tingle in my gut, every single time I hungered desperately for orgasm, every time my dick got hard all by itself, I thought of Jesus hanging naked and bleeding on the cross for my sins. My awful sins.

That did not stop me from solo sex. But for years afterward, I never saw a crucifix without getting an erection.

Because of jokers like Mr. Coons—untold numbers of them—solo sex shame is almost universal. I belong to a boating club. (They call it a yacht club, but if you saw these yachts you'd realize it's a boating club.) About a year ago, I was taking some supplies aboard my boat when Mike, who has the slip next to mine, stepped over the rail onto the walkway separating the boats. He's about twenty-six, good looking, well educated, a physical education teacher. I decided to get some material for a lecture I was giving a few weeks later. I greeted him. We shook hands. Then I asked, "Do you masturbate?"

He took a step back and almost fell into the river. "Hell, no," he exclaimed. Then, recognizing my scowl, he averted his eyes and said, "Well, only when my girl's not around."

"How often isn't she around?"

He cleared his throat, and answered, "Maybe twice a day."

You might think that those who claim faith in traditional religions—that God made humankind, their bodies, their sexualities, and found that all he had made "was very good"—would rejoice in sex and solo sex. You might think that gay men and women would be in the forefront of such open-minded rejoicing. You might be wrong.

Four years ago, I spoke at a discussion group for a local Metropolitan Community Church. Its doctrines are similar to those of Baptists, except that the congregation is made up primarily of gay, bisexual, and lesbian people. Curiously, I was invited to talk about sex, and so, to warm things up quickly, I began with a question:

"Did Jesus masturbate, or did he have nocturnal emissions—wet dreams? Now, if you believe the Bible—that Jesus was a human being in every way—it must be one or the other. That's the normal function of the male genital system."

I thought the collective gasp created enough vacuum to suck the windows in. Half the audience glared. The other half seemed to be in a state of dissociation. After the service, one sexy young man told me, "That thing about Jesus and masturbation—that was heresy. You could go to hell for that."

Even that virtually extinct species, the Intelligent Fundamentalist, recognizes the innate rightness of solo sex. More than a year ago now I did an article on teenage sex and the fact that society condemns fucking while offering no alternative. I called Doug Long, youth director for a fundamentalist church in eastern Pennsylvania, and asked, "How are young people to release sexual tension?"

"The Bible is absolute," he explained. "There can be no sex apart from marriage." (That, of course, is the official position of every Roman Catholic and orthodox Protestant church in America, not to mention those of the Islamic faith.)

"I know that's the party line," I told him, "but when the need gets too strong, and you can't concentrate on school work and you're really just climbing the walls—what then?"

"God will give you the power. He says we're 'not tempted above that we are able. He will, with the temptation, also give us a way to escape.'"

"Masturbation?" I suggested eagerly.

"Masturbation is *sin*."

"Doug, I never knew anybody in my life, and I'll bet you didn't either, including you and me, who from the ages of thirteen to nineteen never had any sexual release but a wet dream. You mean what we did was a *sin*?"

The question made Doug uneasy.

"Well, if you could masturbate with a clean mind, that would be fine. The Bible says, 'Whatsoever things are good, whatsoever things are pure...think on these things.' If he could do that, all right."

Like I say, whenever I think of Christ on the cross, I get an erection. Is that clean enough?

Let me share with you my theory about why organized religions are so opposed to sex. And let me do it by playing a game with you: Let's pretend we have just taken over the leadership of a Church. We didn't originate it, mind you—that was done a few centuries ago by people who were full of genuine conviction. In fact, they died for their faith, and when they weren't dying they were celebrating their lives—being baptized nude, washing each other's hair and feet in humility, greeting each other with kisses, procreating in joy. They had no phony sacraments like communion services; according to the teachings of their leader, *whenever* they ate or drank, they did it in his name. They were a happy lot. No wonder thousands and thousands joined them in worship.

But when we take over this Church it's with a new agenda. It's a business, pure and simple. Why the hell should we work for a living when we can run a religion? So we set our goals in order:

1. Money in the offering plates.
2. Devotion of the flock.
3. Money in the pledge envelope.
4. Fifteen hours of work per week, max.
5. Home, car, pension plan.
6. Money in the anonymous donors box.

We're no fools, and we realize at the outset that people aren't just going to give us money without some very good reasons. And that's the work we have cut out for us. We'll make people feel good about themselves. We'll make them feel just great—not only in the eyes of their fellow humans, but in God's eyes as well. We'll sell them salvation!

But to do that, we've got to make them feel lost first. We'll make them feel guilty for doing all sorts of bad things. No killing. No stealing. No lying. No jealousy. No fooling around with the relatives. (That rule alone will push the guilt button of every redneck in Alabama.)

All that will make for a pretty boring existence, so we will require lots of songs about Heaven, and how wonderful life will be *some* day.

But that's still not going to do the trick. Sad to say, there are still a few people here and there who don't kill, steal, lie, get jealous, or fool around with relatives. We need a better sin—a *universal* sin.

And there you have it, folks—the perfect sin, with its theoretically voluntary nature, celebrated by all ancient and primitive religions and now condemned by every fundamentalist sect around the world because it means money: **SEX**.

Yes, sex is the perfect sin. And, unlike our belief in S ta Claus and the Easter Bunny, we never outgrow it.

I was twenty years old and just married for the first time, living in Stroudsburg, Pennsylvania, and I realized I needed to buy some rubber prophylactics, as we called them at the time. So I went to the drug store on Main Street, walked in the front door, and there, all the way in the back, elevated two feet above the floor on a riser and behind a glass panel, stood the pharmacist. His face is riveted into my brain—a goatee, black hair, dark eyes behind thick lenses. He seemed to stare at me as I walked red-faced down that aisle toward him.

"May I help you?" he asked boldly, peering along his beak of a nose to rivet me. I could hardly speak.

"I would like a box of rubber prophylactics," I squeaked.

"What size?"

"About seven inches, I guess."

"What size *box*?"

If you think that sort of sexual embarrassment was then and this is now, you're mistaken. From every corner, big-mouthed, hypocritical adults are yelling, "Abstain! Abstain!" According to the party line, abstinence is the solution to out-of-wedlock pregnancy, venereal disease, AIDS. But the underlying message—the intended one—is that *sex is evil*.

And from whom did this message of abstinence come? Parents forced into wedlock through pregnancy. Fundamentalist Protestant evangelists like Jimmy Swaggart and Jimmie Bakker, founders of religious colleges and universities, whose reputations have been blighted by sexual scandal.

"Abstain!" shouts the priest. Yet, in September, 1990, *Time* quoted researcher Richard Sipe, indicating that twenty percent of all priests have enjoyed an enduring sexual relationship with a woman. Another ten to thirteen percent have done so with men, and six percent with children. Between forty-five and fifty percent of them confessed to being active at the time of the interview—and there's no way of knowing how many were active and lied.

And there's that miserable old Sunday school teacher, Mr. Coons, and his ilk. Easy for them to yell, "Abstain!" when they're so old they can't remember where they left their penises—much less what to do with them, unless there's a kid around.

Pat Buchanan was entirely right when, at the Republican National Convention of 1992, he said, "There is a religious war going on in this country." Anyone who hasn't recognized that by now isn't conscious. Sterile-souled, mean-spirited religionists are launching all-out war against the body and its sacred sexuality. Thanks to them, psychiatrists' offices are crowded with the emotionally wounded and the guilt-ridden. And police precincts across America struggle with the highest sex-crime rate per capita in the *world*.

As I wrote in *The Joy of Solo Sex*, sexual tension will always find release, either through its intended route of coitus or masturbation, or through perversion that may be sexual or social. It may entail rape or child abuse. It may involve murder, vandalism, senseless violence. But there is no exception to the fact that sexual drive will express itself even if it must masquerade to do so.

Police state tactics are used to beat sex-positivists into submission to fundamentalist morality; when the Justice Department attacked the *Adam & Eve* erotic catalog as pornographic in one state and lost, it promptly indicted the company in another state and another and another. Eventually, had a federal judge not quashed the Justice Department's program of persecution, the company would have gone bankrupt proving its innocence.

More efforts are being made to outlaw nudism in the out-of-doors. Although the Bible tells us that Adam and Eve were created nude in the Garden, and that it was Adam's shame, not God's will, that led to the fig leaf incident; although several prophets of the Old Testament wandered naked for years declaring their messages; although we are told in the scriptures that we came naked into the world and shall leave it naked—apparently wandering the streets of Heaven the way God made us—nude is equated with lewd in the eyes of the damning fundamentalists.

It's an intolerable situation pure and simple, and the first step in changing it is to recognize that we are, indeed, at war, and the enemies are the same as always—the self-appointed ambassadors of God, the Arthur Comstocks of the world.

The second step is to get intolerant of intolerance, condemn the condemners, and expose the god which these people have made in their own image, the mass-marketed, big-bucks, soda pop god of the sawdust trail. What audacity that anyone should think he can understand the mind of God Almighty!

Perhaps you're aware that there is a strong movement underway in the United States toward recognizing a God of the Body, with such proponents as Andrew Greeley, Matthew Fox, Georg Feuerstein, David Steinberg, Brenda Tattlebaum, Joani Blank, Sally Miller and Robert Bahr, among many others. These people are saying that the choice isn't God *or* the Gonads. It's the God of the Gonads against the bloody, violent god of the Crusades, the witch burnings, flagellants and self-castrating Skopts. These people are advocating a body-centered faith in which sex is sacred and orgasm a sacrament.

I promise you this book is not a political diatribe. But my experience is that many of you need to hear these words, to recommit yourself to a fully liberating spirit of sexual positivism, before reading further. (And besides, I really did have to get it out of my system!) Let me close with these words by Gunnar Eklof:

Ex Ponto

One must have the courage to break the commandments
That say that the sun doesn't also circle the Earth,
That the blood doesn't also rejoice in sorrow without shame,
That wine isn't wonderful for the heart,
That the body's pleasure isn't also the soul's,
The soul and the body aren't the inside and the outside,
But are *veramente* one and the same.

Chapter Two

Positive Narcissism

It never occurred to me, in writing *The Joy of Solo Sex*, that there could be such a thing as too much self love—but that question has been raised, and I think we must deal with it at the outset. I had always felt that self-love was the essence of emotional health and stability, and in fact was the basis of a caring relationship to others. I confess that it was not an original idea. I lifted it from Jesus, who told us that the entire Mosaic law is fulfilled in "loving the Lord thy God with all thy heart, soul, and mind," and, more to the point, "loving thy neighbor as *thyself*." The wellspring of love for others is love of self.

Is it possible to love oneself too much? Specifically, can one be attracted to one's own being sexually to the point that it's emotionally damaging? A number of men have written asking precisely that. So the logical place to begin, it seems, is with the testimonies of men who expressed profound self-love—particularly in terms of the erotic. Here's what Julian, from New York, wrote:

27

I'm a super-masturbator, a confirmed solosexualist and always have been—it's the greatest! But first, I want to ask you a question. Reading a lot of your newsletters, it seems to me that you don't ever use the word *narcissism*. I understand that many solosexualists are not narcissistically inclined but I am, totally, and so are lots of others, especially gay guys, and I love being like this. I don't think there's anything wrong with it, do you?

So this is my story. I'm handsome, athletic, slim, sexy, with a beautiful big dick and huge low-hanging balls which I completely worship. I'm totally turned on by my own body, and my image in the mirror is the most handsome and sexy guy I've ever known. And I'm very much in love with myself. I do like having sex with others—mostly men and occasionally women —but when I do, I'm really thinking of me all the time and I'm enjoying me most of all.

But always, sex with me alone is by far the best and most beautiful. I love phone sex with other narcissistic guys, doing the same thing, both of us describing to the other how terrific we are and how we both worship ourselves, particularly our penises and balls. I jack off a tremendous amount, usually with grease, mirrors (and sometimes with poppers) and I often worship myself like this for hours. I often spend a whole wonderful evening with just me alone, making love to myself and reveling in the beauty of my body in lots of different positions.

One wall of my bedroom is completely mirrored and what is really great (and I recommend it to every guy like me) is a four-foot by one-foot mirror in a light frame which I can move about anywhere (about $10.00 or so from any Woolworth's or similar store— absolutely the greatest buy imaginable!) I put it in all sorts of positions so that, reflecting in the big wall mirror, I see various images of me in several different positions at the same time: standing up, sitting on the side of my bed or lying down—all of which is a terrific turn-on. Sometimes, lying on the bed, I have this mirror at my side, kissing myself passionately, and sometimes, lying on my back, holding it above my body, then gradually lowering it to myself until our lips, tongues, and bodies meet.

An evening with myself, naked, unashamed, and totally in love is truly blissful, the best sex I could ever imagine.

Probably there are many like me (I'm in contact with quite a few), but I wish a lot of us could all get together in some sort of club, or in a gathering somewhere, all of us making passionate love to ourselves, which would be fantastic! Is such narcissism healthy?

It's a worthwhile question. People everywhere seem concerned that they might deviate in some way from the masses, might look different, or act eccentric. And this high school mentality has us thinking that deviation and eccentricity are by definition negative. I wondered about it myself when I finished *The Joy of Solo Sex*, and so I asked a colleague, a prominent psychologist with whom I had co-authored a previous book, to read my latest one.

He responded in amazement that such a sexually liberating and honest volume was in print anywhere, much less the United States. But he had some hesitation about forthrightly praising it. The problem? "Well, it's...narcissistic," he said.

"Is that unhealthy?"

"Certainly. Well, I'm not sure. No. Yes."

Narcissus was the golden-haired youth of Greek legend who refused the advances of the nymph Echo and other desirable females. One day, walking in the woods and coming upon a pool, he did discover the person whom he would love eternally—a reflection in the water of his own beauty. But attempts to embrace himself proved impossible, and he died of languor, pining away over his unfulfilled desire.

Havelock Ellis first used the term narcissism to describe a case of male autoeroticism. Yet, to this day, there is no consensus among psychotherapists regarding a *definition* of the term, much less whether it's a hallmark of emotional health or disease.

For example, Paul Federn, MD, writes in *Ego Psychology And The Psychoses*, "Narcissism is autoeroticism raised to the mental level." In other words, narcissism is intellectual masturbation. Others have called it "a concentration of psychological interest upon the self," "an inability to distinguish the self from the outside world, as an infant makes no distinction between himself, his mother and a bottle of milk."

In fact, there is no universally agreed upon definition of narcissism.

Nor are the professionals in harmony about the characteristics of the narcissist. Elsa Ronningstam, Ph.D., writes in *The American Journal of Psychiatry* that those with "narcissistic personality disorders" have a "sense of superiority, a sense of uniqueness, exaggeration of talents, boastful and pretentious behavior, grandiose fantasies, self-centered and self-referential behavior, a need for attention and admiration, arrogant and haughty behavior..."

Remind you of Rush Limbaugh?

When it comes to morality, the narcissist believes that his insights take precedence over the law—even the Constitution of the United States, as in Oliver North.

Salman Akahtar, MD, writes of the narcissist's profound anger. "The irrationality of this vengeful attitude is frightening because it is not only intact but sharpened."

But, in one of the few thorough studies of narcissistic personality disorder, Elsa Ronningstam found that narcissists did better at their jobs, fewer were institutionalized in mental hospitals, and they "had significantly higher achievement." Of course they didn't mind telling others just how successful they were.

Narcissists and Sex

Then there's the matter of narcissists and sex. Dr. Karl Menninger, in *Man Against Himself,* said of narcissists, "they are very proud of their sexual organs and, indeed, it is not inaccurate to say that such persons prefer masturbation to sexual intercourse. Such intercourse as they perform is frequently only a kind of intravaginal masturbation..."

Salman Akahtar, MD, writes in *The American Journal of Psychiatry,* "their [narcissists'] lack of empathy is often most apparent in their sexuality. Intercourse is a purely physical pleasure, the partner being less a person than a means to an end."

He adds, "there is also a tendency toward sexual promiscuity, homosexuality, perversions..."

So: Narcissists have sex only with themselves. Or with women who are not people but masturbation devices. Or with women, men, and whatever. The professionals offer contradictory descriptions of narcissistic sexuality.

Who are the narcissists? Gregory Zilboorg wrote many years ago in *The Atlantic Monthly* that they included Jack London, Richard Wagner, Schopenhauer, Tchaikovsky, Nietzsche, Guy de Maupassant, Tolstoy, and others.

Shakespeare, too, was narcissistic. In fact he wrote a sonnet (number 62) to self-love:

Sin of self love possesseth all mine eye
And all my soul and all my every part;
And for this sin there is no remedy,
It is so grounded in word in my heart.
Me thinks no face so gracious as is mine,
No shape so true, no truth of such account,

31

And for myself mine own worth do define,
As I all other in all worths surmount.

It's true, of course—as Benjamin Franklin said—"He who loves himself will have no competition." But it's also true, in Voltaire's words, that, "Self-love is the instrument of our preservation; it resembles a provision for the perpetuity of mankind—it is necessary, it is dear to us, it gives us pleasure, and we must possess it."

The *Talmud* says, "Every man has the right to feel that, 'Because of me was the world created.'" And in Erich Fromm's words, "If an individual is able to love productively, he loves himself, too; if he can love only others, he cannot love at all."

The nature of humanity is to condemn that which is different from the ordinary. (In fact, it's a characteristic of other species as well.) If you don't worship my god in my way, you're a heretic and ought to be burned at the stake. If you march to the beat of a different moral drummer, if you practice sex differently, if you dress differently, if you speak differently, you're to be condemned. It's the same with narcissism; in a world where most people dislike themselves for being too fat, skinny, small-dicked, flat-titted, bearing a crooked nose or big ears, how could the solosexual narcissist *not* raise eyebrows, even among such learned colleagues as my psychiatrist friend? There's nothing wrong with the pursuit of happiness—in fact, theoretically at least, it's guaranteed by the Constitution. Only when 1) self-love interferes with others' happiness or 2) our own ability to function adequately in the world is it a problem.

In fact, an outwardly-embracing self-love might well be the standard of emotional health that all humankind should seek. At least in my personal experience, those who love others most deeply and selflessly are also most passionately in love with themselves on all levels.

But I want to offer a different line of thought entirely, not one that justifies sexual love in the context that we ordinarily define it, that of everyday heterosexual or homosexual life, but in a completely different way of thinking—that of solosexuality as a valid and flourishing lifestyle. And, just as I can't take credit for originating the idea of loving your neighbor as *your-self*, I must credit this insight to a reader of *CELEBRATE The Self*. Here's what Robert P. of Vermont wrote:

Of all the sexual persuasions in today's society, probably the least recognized as well as the least understood is that of solosexuality. We have the heterosexuals, the bisexuals, the asexuals, the transsexuals and the homosexuals, and even the so called "try-sexuals," and I am sure several other "sexuals" that I have overlooked or don't even know about. But what about us solosexuals?

A true solosexual is hard to find, and yet we are not that uncommon, the reason being that few ever admit to being solosexual. Yet, so far as I am aware, there is no great social stigma against being solosexual, as there is with a few of the other "sexuals." I don't recall ever seeing or hearing of any groups organized and carrying placards pleading for us to "Help us Stamp out Solosexuality today—Save our Children!"

Actually, until quite recently there was no particular name for what I call solosexuality. Most were unaware that such a category might even exist, and even now the name is mostly my arbitrary choice. I really love the name, and while masturbation is, to me, the most beautiful word in the English language, solosexuality seems to connote more of what it really is, or at least what I really am. Masturbation seems to me to mean more one of those now and then, "out of desperation jack-offs" that most ordinary "normal" people indulge in when no other sex is at hand.

Not long ago, a true solosexualist might have classified himself as a "J/O artist," a "Jerk-off freak," or even as a masturbationist. For the great majority, solosexuality as a sexual persuasion is inconceivable, and solo sex is generally thought of as a secondary sexual diversion, not a full-time, full-fledged sexual instinct! Masturbation is one sexual activity which about 99 percent of the population indulges in (rarely at length), but about one percent will admit to.

But remember that masturbation is not necessarily solosexuality—the two are entirely different things. Sure, a solosexual will masturbate, but a hit-and-miss masturbator is rarely a solosexual. Mr. Kinsey did some very interesting research on masturbation, but I don't think he ever realized that true solosexuality even existed. When his book was first published it created quite a stir—especially on the subject of masturbation as well as homosexuality. Of course what was startling then is, today, common knowledge, but solosexuality is still not common knowledge.

I remember when, as a small child, I would play in the bushes or out in the "shack" with the other boys in the neighborhood. We would frequently "circle jerk" and once in a long while a couple of us would "do" each other, but they outgrew those childish games and investigations.

When all the other guys began dating and bragging about their conquests, that is when I knew for sure that I was somehow not like them. Some boys did seem to attract me, but I was barely aware of the attraction and more and more into myself all the time. I did begin to have sexual experience with other young men my age when I was in college but it was always being with myself that I longed for more than anything else. Then I didn't realize that I was solosexual—I just thought I was a very shy homosexual who loved to J/O. I was unaware that I was well on my way in pursuit of my true sexuality, solosexuality.

I remember years before puberty how I would hide myself away in our garage or basement and perform all sorts of rather painful and sexually outrageous things on myself. I remember one little exercise in particular, in which I would take an old double-bell windup alarm clock and, with a string, tie it to my cock. I would slipknot it securely behind the flange of my little boy cockhead and then, stark naked, would stand before an old mirror and get the clock swinging between my legs, agonizing with the resulting pain and pleasure and loving each arc of the swing as it increased the no-nonsense bite of the slipknot. Before starting the swing exercise I would have set the clock's alarm to go off within five or ten minutes, and then, just when I thought I couldn't stand it another second, the big double bell alarm would go off and the vibrations would pound through my super hard little tortured cock and send me into orgasmic spasms of incredible joy.

Today an orgasm of that intensity would probably give me cause to dial 911. Those orgasms have never, never been equaled, although I've sure tried—and of course those were all dry runs. It would be a long time yet before I would be able to "pop" a load, or "spit," as the boys called it then.

I repeated this little ritual over and over until a new compulsive-obsessive exercise was invented or discovered. How many other little boys at ten years or so were playing with themselves like this? I don't think that thought ever entered my mind then, but I knew then that plain old "jerking" was a bore and I was completely fascinated with all the wonderful ways I could find to get myself off....

Now we solos are beginning to come tumbling out, due partly to publications like *CELEBRATE The Self*. The flood gates are opening and we may finally be accepted as being a part of a tried and true sexuality.

Another reader wrote, "Most real solosexuals don't fantasize about other people or times or places. When into a good session I am aware only of what is giving me physical or spiritual gratification at the moment. Yes, I said spiritual. It's the feel of the moment that I'm into and not some other moment at another time—I remain in the immediate present, at oneness with the Universe and/or God! The usual whack-offer is most likely dancing to a tune of another day, but with me it's the here and now. I'm in heaven, pure heaven, nowhere else, no one else.

"Now and then I have been free to spend a few days with myself and I have spent this time totally into myself, only stopping for a rest and a little food now and then. I have kept at myself until I have been forced to stop from sheer exhaustion. I don't waste time nor energy—popping loads; I bring myself to that abyss of oneness, hold and drift back again and again to that indescribably beautiful point of oneness and orgasm. Who could ever do this for me!...

"I frequently bring myself this far and then completely back off, this state of bliss that I have when refusing to cross the finish line. I am overcome with love. I am *love*! I gaze upon the face of God, my own body—I am beautiful, I am hot, I am loved and loving.

"I kiss my own lips and lust for myself totally. I need nothing more, I need no one else now or ever! At this point I am also a little delirious! I am mine, I am solosexual, and I love it."

These men said, in effect, "Of course! I've always been a sexual loner, happiest with myself. Why can't it be that one man has the genes and brain make-up to be attracted to women, others to men, and still others to themselves? Might there not be some benefits to society from men who choose not to relate sexually to others, and yet still know exquisite joy?"

I can hear my psychiatrist colleague saying, "Solosexuals, if there are such things, are abnormal. It's the normal function of the species to propagate [what about homosexuals?], or at least to relate to other human beings sexually." Here are my responses:

—Why? Just why is one normal/emotionally healthy if he relates to others sexually, and abnormal if he doesn't? Are old maids abnormal? Priests? (I'm talking about those few who do refrain from sex with others.) Nuns? Just exactly what emotional or physical malfunction accompanies not having sex with another human being?

—Whether a man has sex with others or not, he has most of his orgasms alone, usually while fantasizing about others. All that separates the solosexual from others is quantity, not quality.

—The world is grotesquely overpopulated right now. Nations are literally starving to death. It may be that solosexuals are a mutation (I did not say a higher life form), the result of which will be to reduce birth rates and thus preserve the species.

To summarize, it is time—actually, long past the time—that we stop condemning people simply by calling them names. We have done that with Jews and Blacks and Hispanics and Puerto Ricans and WASPs and Homosexuals and God knows how many others, and now at least my psychiatrist colleague is happy to do the same with solosexuals, calling them narcissists. But a Jew isn't inferior because he is a Jew, and a homosexual isn't inferior because he's homosexual, and no one is a lesser person because of who they are or what they do *unless they are thereby damaging themselves or society*.

Just as some men are instinctively turned on by women, others by men, others know ecstasy by turning in upon themselves, their fantasies, their games. Some children enjoy playing by themselves. Some men enjoy solo sex. As long as it doesn't interfere with other relationships, the ability to hold a job, to

37

maintain a reasonable standard of living, and relate functionally to the world around them, solosexuals are but another facet in the glorious gem of human sexuality.

Chapter Three

Dancing on the Edge

T.J., of Chester, Vermont, writes, "I sink down to my knees, spreading my butt and now clenching my stomach muscles to pump more blood into my raging hot and hard dick, until my breath breaks and I pant in air. I've got a real cycle going now, and I can only get hotter with just the lightest fondling of my intrepid shaft. For the next hour or so, I'll be high on my own body chemistry and will break only if I have to...

"Take it to the edge and back off maybe sixty to seventy times. By now, I know exactly what I want and I give it to myself stroke by stroke, but I've been at it for three or four hours and I feel it's time to back off—I know I can get high again whenever I want, which will most likely be at 3:00 or 7:00 at night."

That's an excellent example of one form of dancing on the edge—or what the insiders call brinkmanship. According to Allen Erich, Editor of *CELEBRATE The Self* Newsletter, more readers write about this solosex variation than any other.

The meaning of brinkmanship should be self-evident. Yet, there are at least three variations of the practice, each offering a different kind of pleasure and fulfillment.

The Whole-Body High

Sales pitches and misconceptions notwithstanding, the whole-body high is not a penile orgasm that radiates through your whole body. In fact, using the word *orgasm* is clearly misleading. It is, pure and simple, an endorphin-induced euphoria. (Endorphins are opiate-like neurotransmitters produced by our bodies under stress such as the stress of hungering for and being denied sexual release.) Here's a testimonial of how brinkmanship can lead to the whole-body high:

Within the last year I have really learned how to enjoy stroking my penis for hours on some occasions, as I am doing right now. I started last evening about 10 PM when I had a hard-on. I stroked myself for two hours and then decided I wanted to go to sleep. At that point my entire body was so turned on that, after stopping stroking myself and just breathing, I continued to enjoy, with each breath, a very nice mellow flow of sexual energy throughout my entire body. Like the waves of the ocean, the sexual flow takes on one feeling with the intake of air and a subtle difference on the exhale. I guess I rode those waves for about forty-five minutes before I fell to sleep.

I just lay there enjoying the feeling and began to stroke it, alternating between stroking and just laying there letting the waves of sexual energy flow through my entire body with each breath, while my hands either just held my arms as in an embrace, or with one hand on my face and the other on or massaging my chest.

If there is a reader out there who has never experienced stroking himself for an hour or more, I encourage him to try.

I made a breakthrough in solo sex when I stopped worrying about whether or not I would be able to stop at the brink and concentrated on enjoying pleasure and listening to my body's reactions. I found that, if I just let my hands do what they wanted, they know how to rotate from one movement to another seeking pleasure, and always know how to change the tempo or stroke so as to achieve the greatest pleasure for the longest time.

The continued practice and the focus on pleasure have brought me to the point where I am now. I have enjoyed stroking myself at least an average of thirty minutes each morning and evening, at least six days a week, for months. My last ejaculation was over three weeks ago. More and more time elapses between ejaculations and the pleasure just gets better. The best is yet to come. I have some of my most profound spiritual connections with self, others and the universe during and especially after I have been stroking and playing with myself.   —T.P., IL

This man is describing a genuine, physical euphoria—even ecstasy, depending upon whether the sexual tension triggers release of "enhancing" hormones. They include adrenaline from the adrenal glands, thyroxin from the thyroid, and testosterone from the testes.

What happens is that, as you allow yourself to creep closer and closer to orgasm, your brain interprets the hunger and torturous, unfulfilled longing as it would any other unsatisfied need—for example, hunger or thirst. In the wild—and remember that all of our primitive, basic responses remain "in the wild"—we would need a sustained burst of energy and drive to reach a distant water hole or to kill the prey to sate our appetites. The fact that our "appetite" seeks to satisfy lust changes nothing. The body's response is the same: increased

41

breathing and heart rate, a testosterone bath to the brain to provide the aggression and perhaps rage needed to conquer the enemy, the adrenaline for short-term energy, the thyroxin for sustained effort, and endorphins to counter the stress and possible pain of combat.

Here's what can happen, according to Tim Johnson, of Chester, Vermont:

Having worked myself up to the "kicked in" feeling, I get out of bed and do what has to be done, mostly with one hand. I can let the dog and cat out with one hand and even pour a glass of juice while jerking myself.

In good weather like this, I go out on my porch and kind of salute the morning with a full hard-on. Walking through damp grass sends chills right through my balls and I can feel them ride up. For sport I take a kind of run/walk around the pond, sometimes stopping for power strokes facing the morning sun. Jogging flagellates my erection, slapping it around, making it harder (but not always hotter) and it amuses me. By the time I get around to inspecting the garden, I'm on my cock with both hands. I curve slightly to the left, too, and find my right fist fits best over my left for the ideal stroking. I'm self-lubricating, too, by now, and, mixed with a little dew, I'm getting sublime friction.

Back in the house, I lube up more and check myself out in the mirror. The face and upper chest are red flushed now and my balls are a shiny mahogany color. Now that I've called up the juices in my body, I do a full body massage and a series of Kegels to get my whole body hot.

There is no stopping now, and I draw some shades and turn the phone off for some serious whacking off. By now I'm totally on to myself and need nothing other than my hand and some lubricant. I'll start out standing, feet apart, one hand holding the base of my hard-on and the other jacking the top half, making a ring of my thumb and fore-finger, working my rigid corona. Butt contractions are playing both ends against the middle now and my groin and ass are hot. I'm swaying and bucking now, staring at my cock, swearing at it affectionately and begging for more.

The object is to get my cock and mind in tune. That way anything is possible...

Dancing on the edge has been described repeatedly as making one frantic, frenzied. Yet, precisely this same experience, carefully controlled, was the essence of the ancient Hindu Tantric copulation ritual. It was based on the effort to move sexual energy from the genital up into the various hypothetical energy centers known as Chakras by resisting orgasm while remaining in the throes of lust.

You needn't believe in Chakras, however, to have the same experience as the Hindus did. The man who could keep his erect penis in his partner's body for half an hour would begin to feel his penis glowing. After two hours, that sensation would spread to his abdomen; after three hours it would reach his heart. And after five hours, it would reach his throat.

According to *TANTRA: The Magazine*, "After five hours of stimulation without outward orgasm, the head center will fill with energy. Thoughts will have long disappeared as you bask in pure sensation. You will understand the potential of a full body orgasm that goes on indefinitely.... If you stop at this point without orgasmic release, your body will glow for days and you will float on air."

Gliding Over The Edge

Have you ever, just to find out how intense an orgasm can really be, pumped as fast and as violently as you could all the way through the ejaculation? The pleasure is so intense that it's almost painful, and perhaps you think, I can't stand another second of this. And yet you keep going until it's over, leaving you shriveled and fatigued.

Gliding Over The Edge is precisely the opposite of that. You approach the orgasm gradually and in complete control, never losing sight of your goal. That goal isn't to avoid orgasm, but the prostate spasms that almost always accompany ejaculations. In fact, in Gliding Over The Edge, both orgasm and actual loss of seminal fluid do occur, but not as they would in a completely fulfilling orgasm that includes prostate spasms, resolution, and detumescence. Here's how J.B. of New Jersey describes it:

"[For this experience,] I stroke myself slowly and steadily for at least half an hour, until I reach that point where my cock cries 'Stop or I'll shoot!' I know from experience that he means what he says. I stop, relax, and he backs off. Then I feel semen rising up through my urethra with about the same force as urine flow. It comes out not as hurled gobs, but as a gently steady stream that courses downward over the cantle of my generous glans, then the swollen cock shaft, to collect in my thick pubic hair.

"Then, without losing either my erection or the urgent desire to continue stroking my cock, I can achieve from three to seven (my record to date) orgasms, each one involving the loss of what seems to be a normal volume of semen for a full ejaculation, but which does not leave me feeling that I have reached the final climax. If I am very careful, these ejaculations occur at about five minute intervals—sometimes the intervals are shorter. During the whole time—from the first ejaculation to last—I am experiencing a high that is little short of complete orgasm."

The trick here is, first, to get the body to a state of hyperarousal, and maintain that condition for at least half an hour. That will have the effect of "tricking" the prostate—its ejaculation response will be desensitized. It's like the boy who cried wolf—after half an hour of false messages, the prostate isn't as sensitive as you approach the edge even though this time you intend to go glide over it.

However, there are two ejaculatory orifices that allow semen to empty into the urethra. Usually, they remain tightly closed to prevent loss of semen during urination—or, while going around your daily business. But, as orgasm approaches, these orifices relax. Although that usually coincides with prostatic spasms, some fluid can escape without the contractions.

To master this type of brinkmanship requires two qualities: 1) Exquisite control of genital function, knowing just when to back off in order to avoid prostate spasms. That kind of self-knowledge requires years of practice for most men. 2) A stronger than average lust level. It takes effort and determination to come back for a second or third—or seventh!—orgasm before feeling satisfied.

The Extended Orgasm

The third form of brinkmanship is neither a high nor a series of orgasms but an extended penile orgasm, like a surfer riding the crest of a wave, and can extend for minutes. It does not include ejaculation, and, although it's blissful beyond imagination, it isn't as devastating—in the positive sense—as a usual orgasm.

Here's how one man describes the experience:

One delightful day a few years ago I made the stupendous discovery that I could spend hours and hours soloing on the ecstatic front edge of orgasm. Don't misunderstand, I love every minute of the many times that I have soloed for a few hours here and there previously, but they were clumsy efforts by comparison. I have known for some time that I am able to keep a very firm erection all day by rubbing to the brink and then backing away. By doing this up and back down cycle repeatedly, I've enjoyed many long, blissful hours of pure pleasure, excitement, even fulfillment.

The experience I'm talking about goes distinctly beyond what I've described so far. I'm sitting here shivering with delight just to be thinking and writing about it.

I had been performing a beautiful act of self-love for about an hour with many trips to the brink and back. (Hour number one for me is critical. Sometime during that first hour or early in the second, a switch seems to go off that lets me know that I can successfully proceed into a long-term solo.) It was quite by accident, then, that I discovered that, instead of retreating from the brink, I could embrace ecstasy and continue ever so carefully on. It was for me an uncharted course that paralleled the edge of the precipice. One step more and I would be orgasming all over the place; one step back I would be temporarily out of the intense pleasure zone. But I had found a narrow path. I knew ecstasy, and its presence was overwhelming.

I used slow, deliberate strokes or lighter, faster ones, but the important thing was to keep consistent hand contact, anticipate and be responsive to the slightest change in sensation and to keep going. I made sure that my breathing was deep and slow, at an even pace. I was sweating a great deal, even though my skin was cool. I consciously tried to keep muscles relaxed but could only go part way on this. I held my body very still. In order to stretch or move my legs, I slowed down so as to temporarily leave the intense pleasure zone.

The pleasure was indescribable; the gratification, extreme. My whole body seemed to be radiating out of my balls. My penis went beyond doing its usual magnificent throb thing into a much more intense mode of sensation.

At the sides just under the ridge of my cockhead, a certain puffy swelling began to build. (This only happens to me when I've been super excited for a long, long time) The pleasure didn't stop at my cock, nor the now swollen and slick head, nor the tight balls and crinkled sac. *My entire body was steeped in it!* I was wracked with pleasure in the same sense that one can be wracked with pain. Time didn't have a whole lot of meaning to me at that point. I could have stayed there forever.   —Bill P., OH

Another writes, "I have reached a point where I gain an orgasm plateau for as long as five to ten minutes, while all the while constantly jacking. Fantastic!"

Incidentally, if you think this sort of thing is just for the youngsters in the crowd, think again. In fact, the reverse may well be true. This particular gentleman is 72 years old. Learning to dance on the edge may not be an art, but it certainly is a skill, one that young people rarely have the time and patience to develop. Yet, for those who have learned it, few pleasures are more joyful.

Chapter Four

More Toys and Games

I'm talking in generalities—there are always exceptions: The sex lives of most males is beyond a woman's comprehension. She sees an empty toilet tissue cylinder and thinks it's time to buy more. He sees the same object and within five seconds has impaled it with his penis.

She thinks a feather duster is for dusting. He thinks it's for tickling his testicles.

To her, clouds evoke images of the idyllic, pastoral, romantic. To him they're blatant displays of vulvas, breasts, and —most obvious of all—raging, erect phalluses with huge, dangling balls.

Drop a carrot, and before it hits the floor, he'll think of three ways to sexually abuse it. Being practical, she'll wash it off and nibble on it—which is one of the three things he had in mind. The male is obsessed with sex. He will insert his penis into any object that will stand still long enough. He works for money but lives for sex. When he isn't having it, he's thinking of ways to get it, and, if truth be told, he often enjoys himself more alone than with a partner. That's when he gets the chance to pull out all the stops, to experiment and invent and feel both ecstasy and pride in his ingenuity.

In this chapter, I'll present the everyday, the clever, and even the bizarre toys and games that men from many parts of the world have shared with me.

Lubricants And Lotions

Contrary to what you may suspect, not all men use lubricants when practicing solo sex. These men are almost always uncircumcised.

The advantage of the foreskin is that it allows the penis to function according to nature. And this is the point: the glans of an uncircumcised penis for the most part screws its own foreskin, not vaginal or anal walls, or even a hand. (The foreskin doesn't rub against the glans but wraps and unwraps over it.) There is rarely the rubbing of tissue against tissue. Thus, the skin of the glans remains soft and sensitive. Both the evidence and common sense indicate that the glans of an uncircumcised man is more sensitive than that of his circumcised brothers.

Probably as a result, the penises of uncircumcised men are more sensitive to touch. For example, glans-to-tongue fellatio might prove painful rather than pleasurable. Anecdotal information indicates that orgasms might also be more intense, but in a sex-negative society such as ours, no one has undertaken a careful double blind study to prove it.

If you're circumcised and you would like to know what the uncircumcised man feels (taking into account the possible desensitization of nerves in your glans), begin with one of those small white plastic trash bags you use in the bathroom or kitchen waste basket. Get yourself an erection and wet your glans. Now, lay the entire bag like a tent over the head of your penis, draping it around the shaft. Note: you are not putting your penis into the bag. You are putting the unopened bag over the penis.

The moisture will hold the inner side of the bag to the surface of the glans. Gently slide the outer surface back and forth. You'll be enjoying the rubbing effect without the surface-to-surface friction that occurs when the foreskin is removed.

A good lubricant can produce a similar effect. And you don't have to spend ten dollars—or even four dollars and fifty cents for a stingy eight ounces of massage or lubricating oil.

Do-it-yourself creams and lotions are 1) much cheaper; 2) at least as healthy and sometimes more so; and 3) customized to your own tastes and personality.

First, these general points: Don't use petroleum-based products, including Vaseline, if you're planning to use condoms. As most of you know (please, God, I hope!) petroleum eats away at latex, as in condoms, so using such jellies as lubricants can prove deadly. How safe can a product be to my most precious organs when it destroys rubber? Not a single study can I point to in support of my suspicion, but I'll go on using natural, organic products on my favorite organics.

Secondly, the following formulas are not necessarily interchangeable. For example, if you're a really tough dude into new sensations, you might dig a one-part clove oil to five parts olive oil mixture on your cock shaft. But you might howl like hell if you get that same mixture on your nuts or glans (although some guys enjoy the pain). And you would *never, ever use even small amounts of these oils in an anal lubricant.*

Here are some oils that I've used successfully.

The Warming Oils

These are the ones I've just been talking about: eucalyptus, wintergreen, and clove. They can be ordered through most pharmacies, although only wintergreen is likely to be stocked. They cost from about $2.50 for four ounces (wintergreen), to perhaps three times that for the more exotic oils. But you're using so little that it's a real bargain.

You'll also need an ounce of vegetable oil. Any will do, even corn oil. But if you want to do your phallic skin a favor while you're at it, keep in mind that vitamin E is essential to skin health, and, although corn oil is certainly rich in vitamin E at 13 mg/100g, the best if you can find it is cottonseed oil (50mg/100g).

Add to the ounce of oil just 15-20 drops of clove or other oil extract. This will give you a pleasant, glowing feeling, but won't burn unless you're extremely sensitive.

Of course the oil can also be used by itself. Another choice is to add your favorite cologne. I use four drops of Gray Flannel. More than that becomes overwhelming.

You needn't make more than an ounce or two at a time. Oils store well in tiny seasoning jars and can be kept indefinitely. They needn't be refrigerated.

Soothing Lubricants

What most people don't know about expensive hand and body lotions and lubricants is that most of them are little more than perfumed vegetable shortening. One pound of vegetable shortening (Crisco, for example) costs 99 cents. I put five heaping tablespoons in a bowl, stir in two teaspoons of Johnson's Baby Powder, and have enough clean, fresh-smelling lubricant to last me for a couple of months.

In fact, those five tablespoon are more than enough to give a friend a totally satisfying full-body massage. But in that case I would scent the lotion with six drops of Jovan's Musk for Men, or some other favorite sexy fragrance. But no more—the fragrance should not call attention to itself.

Here are some other suggestions offered by my correspondents:

Baby Powder

"I recently discovered something I hadn't done for at least thirty years," writes Wayburne, from Tacoma, WA, "—to jack off with baby power as the lubricant. This one should be done slowly, savoring every sensation. Use plenty of powder, on the balls as well, and keep adding more as is necessary to keep perfectly dry and slippery. Part of the pleasure is as if it would be an itch if it were stronger. And it builds a marvelous climax.

"I find a different sensation, depending on whether the baby powder is made of talc or of corn starch. Talc seems more intense."

In fact, baby power works fine with the foreskin, too. If you have one, pull the foreskin back, powder up generously, and then rub just the glans. You'll get a strange tingling sensation—perhaps you'll find it pleasant, perhaps not—all through your body, and along with it the ecstasy of orgasm.

Coconut Oil/Cream

Here's a really low-cost lotion—between one and two dollars—that has the perfect consistency for pleasure and doesn't turn dry and gritty. Try experimenting, using very little at first, then more and more, until finally your groin is a sloppy mess. Somewhere along that scale from too little to too much you'll find the amount uniquely right for you.

Aloe Vera

As many people know, aloe is a common ingredient in many skin-care and first-aid products. It's healing, soothing, and even relieves sunburn pain. T.R. of Orlando, Florida, has used it many times as a phallic lubricant:

"I have easy access to aloe as it is a common landscape and garden plant here. But northerners should know it is also an easily-grown house plant.

"To prepare the aloe juice, I cut off a couple of fleshy leaves and remove the tip and spiny leave edges using kitchen shears. Next, I lay a sheet of plastic wrap on a cutting board and crush the leaf by running a rolling pin or a wine bottle back and forth several times. The juice extracted is *very* slippery (some would say slimy) and has a consistency not terribly unlike semen itself. I pour the juice into a food storage container and refrigerate if I don't use it immediately (like I could resist!). To reheat, I stick the container in warm water or in the microwave until it is the right temperature. This sounds like a lot of work, but it takes ten minutes, (less than a drive to the bookstore) and besides, my cock is worth it!

"I think those who try it will find that it produces sensation unlike any other lube. It may be necessary to reapply several times during a prolonged session, but I doubt that anyone reading this will mind. Besides, it's good for your dick."

Vick's Vapo Rub

Keith J. of Los Angeles offers a "cheap thrill" that sent shivers of remembered pain from my throat to my groin: "Put a small dab of Vick's Vapo Rub on the bottom of the scrotum before masturbating. It gives an enjoyable, warm, tingling feeling 'down there.'"

The key here is the word *small*. When I was seventeen years old and counseling at a religious summer camp in the Poconos of Pennsylvania, I developed a jock itch. (Incidentally, this is caused by the same fungus as athlete's foot, and can be cured virtually overnight by exactly the same products.)

I went to the nurse's office, but she wasn't there. I decided to medicate myself, I took a gob of Vick's Vapo Rub and rubbed it all around between my thighs and scrotum.

I was very fortunate that afternoon that the entire camp was at the swimming pool, because, when I started up the hill and reached Cherokee One, I ran into the cabin, dropped my shorts, hung my naked balls over the sink and scrubbed like hell.

My own cabin was Cherokee Eleven. When I reached Cherokee Four, I went through the same routine. Again at Cherokee Seven, and made a mad dash to my cabin at the top of the hill. I was certainly sexually inhibited in those days, very body-negative. Yet, I lay in agony for at least half an hour totally naked, praying to God to deliver me from this stupidity.

The moral of that story? When it comes to Vapo Rub, a little dab'll do ya.

If you have an imaginative nature, why not take some of these ideas and build on them? Cod liver oil is slimy and very rich in vitamin A. But personally, having rather sensitive genital nerve centers, I enjoy impaling a clump of gooey uncooked bread dough. (I "season" it with a dab of musk oil, and use a little corn oil in addition to the water to keep sloppy.)

Home-made lubricants aren't just a source of *self*-pleasuring, either. They make wonderful gifts. Steve, from New Orleans, received a container of lubrications from a friend. It was a gift never to be forgotten:

Last night I had one of the best stroke sessions in a long time, and I have Brian to thank for it. About 6 pm I went upstairs to take a shower, fully intending to get hot and sweaty before getting nice and clean. In a few moments I was naked, lying on the bed, my cock hard as stone, begging to be touched.

Usually I like some sort of porn to beat off to, but not last night. None was needed. I stared in wonder at my thick, firm flesh, and at the little white bottle Brian had given me, and all I needed to get my heart pounding and my breathing hard was the thought, echoing through my head, that this was what my friend wanted me to do. This was what he expected, intended, counted on me to do when he gave me that lube.

I twisted off the top, getting more excited every moment, but trying not to go too fast, trying to savor each moment. I had not yet touched my dick, which was pressing up against my stomach and pointed at my face, since the focus of this scene was the lube, the very same stuff (I kept telling myself) that my hot friend Brian squeezes onto his stiff cock when he wants to make his semen fly. So the very first touch my hungry cock felt was a dribble of that clear, viscous liquid, a little trail that I ran slowly up one side of the central ridge of the underside of my penis, leaving a goodly amount on the tip, then back down the other side. Finally, I took it in my hand and began to stroke.

Ever have a session with yourself when you're so hot, so turned on, so excited, that the very first pump on your prick seems to feel as intense as the full ejaculation of an "ordinary" come? This was one. I was in ecstasy, staring wide-eyed at my hand stroking my cock. The lubricant turned out to have just the right consistency for serious jacking, not too thin or too thick.

And Brian...I was wild with excitement from knowing that I was feeling the very same thing he likes to feel, using the very same jack-off lube. That he had given it to me just so I could feel it! I could think of nothing else, and I could see him in my mind's eye, see him masturbating furiously, his dick covered with lubricant, hear him egging me on, saying, "Do it Steve! Pump that fucker, just like me! Let's shoot it together!" I knew that was what he wanted me to do. I knew it! So when the moment came, when I came, coming just like my friend wanted me to, my back arched, my head pushed back into the pillow, my eyes clenched shut. I felt hot sperm splattering all over my body, and I reveled in the feeling. A wonderful orgasm, and I stretched it out as long as I could, milking every drop and every sensation.

Household Toys

Finding solosex toys needn't cost money. In fact, that's part of the fun of it—turning everyday items into erotic play things. How many of us, for example, have made love to small bottles—or in, P.K. Kensington's case, vases? "The wife," Kensington says, "is a passive lover for the most part, so I enjoy my needs alone, with the encouragement of your help and others of like mind.

"I use occasionally, for variety, a flower vase with the proper slope and holed to snugly fit over my penis. Sometimes I use hot water to increase the pleasure as I pump back and forth. I recently purchased a small vase to replace the overly long one I had been using. I found if you put a hollow tube such as a coffee stirrer or straw alongside the penis as you enter, the compacted air in front of your penis is allowed to escape, and it makes smoother going as you contentedly pump away."

The ideal air escape cylinder is a small metal or hard plastic tube the size of a paper or plastic straw, but sturdy enough —that won't be crushed by your expanding penis. You cut the tube at a length that will reach from the bottom of a small, narrow bottle to about an inch beyond the top. Olive bottles are perfect for this purpose. Insert your flaccid organ into the bottle, making sure that your scrotum doesn't block off the outer end of the tube.

As your penis swells, it will force air out of the tube. When you are fully engorged, you will fill the bottle firmly. Plug off the end of the tube completely—bubble gum does nicely—and wear the bottle as long as you like. The vacuum will keep you firm and keep the bottle firmly in place, at least for a while.

Straps

You can spend a lot more than twenty dollars buying "cock harnesses" and other commercial straps—or you can make them yourself. D.S. of Vermont wrote about his homemade testicle and penis straps. He told us he wore them "just because it feels good, but I'm also trying to lengthen my scrotum." Here's his story:

Over the years, I have bought several commercially made straps from men's stores or catalogs, but they usually don't fit the way I'd like, and they charge high prices for them. So I went to a local Salvation Army-type thrift store and bought a couple of vinyl, leather, and stretch belts, and old suspenders. Then at a fabric store I bought some heavy-duty snaps and a little device that you use to attach the snaps to the material. The device consists of a little metal "anvil" that you put the snap in and use a hammer with the "flattener" to widen out the rivet part of the snap to put them on the material. Eight or ten snaps and the "anvil" device cost only about $5, and the belts are only about 50 cents each.

You can cut the belts in lengths you want to go around your testicles or penis and testicles, or for stretchers or spreaders, or around the waist. I have also put snaps on the end of stretch belts so I can hook metal rings on them for genital rings. I have found a type of vinyl that I particularly like and I have made several different length straps out of that. I also like them made from stretch belts or suspenders and have tried putting the snaps in different ways to see what works best for me. You can form any pattern or design you want, and all for just a few cents each.

I should also mention that you need some way to make the holes for the snap parts to fit through when you are mounting them. Any small sharp-pointed awl would do, but I've found that a small leather punch works well to punch the holes where you want them.

The best straps are made of soft leather and have several snaps for various degrees of tension. They should also be available in various widths. Commercial devices fasten around both the scrotum and penile shaft. The thicker the scrotal strap, the more effectively they serve as "ball stretchers." According to one correspondent, "The delightful stimulation and feeling in using such straps is beyond words!"

But those snaps can be a problem! I told one writer, "I have learned everything the hard way. With regard to straps that use snaps, I have mangled the skin of my dick to a bloody pulp when depressing the snaps before removing my penile skin. Much more satisfactory to me is a piece of soft leather with Velcro attached along the entire length of the 'hugger.' With the Velcro, as opposed to snaps, it can be made to fit as tight or as loose as desired. I've made them in widths of one inch, three inches, and the one I use most, which is five inches. These aren't fancy, but they're satisfactory. You can make them yourself." But there's one question that deserves to be asked, and it *has* been:

A year and a half ago, I purchased a combination cock strap/ball stretcher/ball divider. I frequently wear it when enjoying solo sex. I have since bought individual cock straps and another ball stretcher. I have liked the sensations and the prolonged erections these straps have provided. I have even, on rare occasions, worn them to the office. I enjoy the feel of a slightly hard cock when I'm going about my day-to-day business.

My question for Dr. Litten involves possible dangers brought about by wearing these straps. Sometimes my balls darken noticeably. I take the straps off when this happens. Three months ago I was hospitalized for blood clots in my lungs. I wonder if they could have been caused by shutting down the flow of blood to my penis and balls. I asked one of my physicians and he said no (but seemed very embarrassed by the question, so I'm not sure he understood what I was asking).

I told myself that the wise thing to do was throw the straps away, but of course I haven't done that. I still enjoy them several times a week. Am I risking my health?   —R.P., MS

My answer: The body has effective mechanisms to prevent blood clotting and coagulation in the absence of oxygen, whether or not the blood flow is restricted. As we age, however, systems don't always work as they should.

When blood ceases to circulate for prolonged periods, there is always the possibility that clots can form. You say that your balls darken noticeably at times—which means that the blood close to the surface of the scrotum has ceased circulating and that the tissue is being oxygen-starved.

The solution, as I stressed in *The Joy of Solo Sex*, is in moderation. Although I am not a medical doctor, I believe that using very tight straps for ten minutes or less is relatively safe, and snug but not tight straps could be left in place much longer. The warning sign is a change in tissue color, indicating that the blood is not flowing.

If you are in good health, you might also consider taking one baby aspirin a day as an antidote to clotting.

Rings

The list is virtually endless:

Napkin rings (made of wood, metal, porcelain, plastic, whose inner dimensions vary from an inch and a quarter to an inch and three quarters.)

—Key rings, both hinged and non-hinged.

—Ball bearing rollers for transmissions (diameter of one and one-eighth inches, pleasantly heavy.)

—Polyurethane pipe. Various sizes. One and one-quarter inches fits nicely. The elbow connector is a particularly interesting piece, since it tilts the wearer's phallus outward and upward. The larger two-inch pipe can fit snugly around testicles, the section to be cut as long as the wearer can endure the stretch. Holes can be drilled through the sides and a cord strung through and tied after the apparatus is in place to keep pressure on the testicles snug and prevent them from escaping. Finally, a larger hole can be drilled through the center and the penis slipped through that while the testicles are pulled out through the bottom and the cord tightened.

—Clamps used in electrical and plumbing work. These are tightened by screws on each end, but let the wearer beware— penile skin caught in the thread of the screws as they tighten will bleed and ache profoundly. It is definitely an experience to avoid.

My all-time favorite ring device is the bicycle inner tube. By cutting rings of various widths, you can find the size that fits snugly without struggling through an endurance trial. These huggers also expand as you do, and are easy enough to remove if necessary, even if you're still in an expansive state.

And that *is* something to consider. Now and again an article will appear in a medical journal explaining precisely how Dr. So-And-So helped some sad soul rescue his precious toy from the tail pipe of a car or some such. As they say in the military, when you go into a tight situation, make sure you have a plan for getting back out.

Feather Duster

"Talk about serendipity!" wrote J.O.T. of Arlington, Virginia. "A neighbor lady, who is very thoughtful and interested in helping everybody, presented me with a Chinese feather duster so that I might 'simplify' my dusting and get into otherwise difficult corners to clean. It is a multi-colored, nylon-type feather duster, about two feet long and I would say about a foot in circumference. When I touched it, it felt so soft and yet firm on my fingers—its multi-colors were a kind of 'turn on' and, you guessed it, I wondered (like I do about a lot of things) how this little beauty would feel on the head of my hard cock.

"I did not lose much time in finding out. I stripped, put a tight cock ring around the base of my dick and, when completely erect, I rolled back my foreskin as far as I could get it to go down my shaft, totally exposing my cock head and about three inches below it, all very tender and tingling with excitement and pleasure. I merely laid back, placed the duster over my dick and began a thrusting of it up and down over the glans and back again, slowly at first, then faster and faster until the ecstasy was intense and I was near shooting. I did not want to put a load into the delicate and lovely 'feathers,' so I stopped, cooled down and started all over again.

"I cannot explain how different this type of stroking felt... I have used many things on my dick head for pleasure but somehow this duster, the soft yet firm, almost slippery strands making it up, felt better going over my dick than anything ever before. One can do it for hours (I often do), and the pleasure seems to get more intense with time. The duster can be purchased, I found out, at any Chinese store selling novelties. I wonder if its maker ever dreamed of the use I have put it to— and the ecstasy it has afforded me. And it costs only $3.00."

I personally had never tried feather dusters, so I bought one a the local supermarket in the hardware section as soon as I read J.O.T.'s description, went home, stripped, and ran it up my inner thighs. It made me *shiver*! I brushed it across my chest, my face. The only thing like it was when, years ago, a lover caressed my body, front and back, with her long hair.

I tried that feather duster on the same partner. She couldn't handle it at first—kept giggling, spasming, especially when it touched lightly the inside of her arms and thighs and the back of her knees. Finally, she calmed down, opened up, and got off.

A young man I used it with was not quite so giddy. I think he's in love—not with me, but my feather duster. But I should caution you that mine was made of real feathers, not multi-colored plastic ones, and it did not stand up to frequent use. After several weeks, the feathers began crumbling, and finally it became so messy that I threw it out.

Condoms

For many men, condoms are a sex toy:

"Although I had a vasectomy years ago, every once in a while I like the feel of a rubber on me when I play, and it is fun to see the load in the end of the rubber after I come."—Don, Port Arthur, Texas.

"Try the ribbed or textured ones. Lightly lubricate your penis before you slip one on. And then use long, slow, fluid strokes, up and down, from top to bottom—K.J., Los Angeles

"Occasionally I like to jack off while using a non-lubri-cated reservoir-tipped rubber. I begin by stroking my cock and finally my balls until I am fully erect and oozing pre-cum. I will then roll the rubber down my shaft and continue to slowly pump my cock and fondle my balls. I will reach a point where the tip of the rubber becomes loaded with my pre-cum. I will slide the end of the rubber over my glans—the rubber is now very slippery and provides great stimulation to the glans. When I finally come, I enjoy watching my cum shoot into the end of the rubber, distending and swelling the tip."

—Frank, Gainesville, Florida

But for others, it's more than an occasional variation—condoms are an integral part of their play time. R.B., of San Diego writes:

From the very beginning, I always made it a practice to use rubbers, be it mutual J/O, oral sex or anal, and very rarely did I have anyone object. For many, it was a "first time," and nine out of ten of them liked it!

I've "dug" rubbers—a fetish, I suppose you could call it—since I was 16, and if I had a dollar for every guy I've "baptized" into using them, I could buy the Vatican! Over the years I've had plenty of guys tell me they enjoy using them, but they seem to feel others will think it's "vanilla sex" or "juvenile." I can't imagine why. What in Holy Hell could be any more butch or masculine than a rubber? It's as masculine as boots, leather jackets, cock rings, tight Levi's, jockstraps, western gear...

Rarely, and I do mean rarely, do you find an article written by a guy describing his fun with sex toys, whether store bought or homemade, and we all know that thousands of guys use their sex toys. But they rarely write about it. I know that over the years I've had a helluva lot of fun using jac-pacs, vibrators, artificial vaginas, inflatable dolls, accu-jacs. I always wore rubbers when using them for two reasons: one, I like the looks and feel of the rubber; plus, when you are finished, there's practically no mess to clean up. I can't be the only guy who enjoyed my sex toys. There must be thousands of others out there that did, too.

Water, Showers, Tubs

Imagine a tribe of primitive humans coming upon a delightful, secluded waterfall. Men, women, children all dive in and enjoy the refreshing water of the pond. Their wandering, nomadic life has rendered them thirsty, dirty, and fatigued. But all at once the men beneath the falls become invigorated. Although, because they were exhausted, they have ignored their wives for weeks, they are suddenly proudly erect. A few moments longer and, one by one, each is swept into the throes of orgasm by the falling water.

I can't prove it, but it's my guess that's how men discovered that water can be erotic.

After a disastrous marriage, one man wrote that, while living alone, he discovered that masturbation was better than a whole lot of things—"like TV, jogging, swimming, movies, and to some extent sleeping and eating. No big surprise there. I had masturbated a lot my whole life, but I was beginning to acknowledge to myself that self-sex had been my staple kind of sex life all along and was likely to continue as such for the rest of my life." He continues:

> I began to devour printed sex and finally came to *The Sensuous Woman* by "J" which brings me to where I was headed as the best way of knowing one's own sexual needs and preferences. "J" suggested removing the shower head and positioning the clitoris in the solid stream of water. I slowly and carefully pondered this concept for two or three seconds—then went in there, unscrewed the shower head and had *my* "clit" (that incredible spot right under the tip) in the stream before I even had time to get hard thinking about it!

> Shattering, mind-boggling orgasm in about 15 or 20 seconds!

> As it turned out, sneaking up on my cock *before* I got hard was sort of the key to success. If I did this it was easy to turn my cock over enough to expose the underside of the tip to the water and the orgasm was so sudden I was usually not hard yet when it was all over. If you're already hard when you step into the

shower, don't despair. You *will* find a way to make it work, as I had to on several occasions! If you're in a shower stall, lean back against the back wall. If you're in a tub, do as "J" instructed the ladies and lie down.

Either way, pull your cock down against your belly so the thudding stream of water hits your favorite place. If you're one of the lucky ones whose hard cock is already flat against your belly, you may only have to steady it a bit in the stream. This is a bit awkward compared to just rolling it over soft, and I think the orgasm is a bit more intense in the soft cock. Maybe because the pulsations of water can penetrate deeper into the soft cock.

I lived in the apartment for another seven years before my present wife and I decided it was safe to move in together... About a year before I moved out, the girl next door said she had often gotten a kick out of hearing me get off in the shower. (I hadn't realized I'd been that noisy!)

R.P. from Mississippi responded immediately: "The use of the shower as a means of masturbation related by T.R.H. made me remember the pleasure I had experienced a few years ago when I owned a jacuzzi. The gushing water and the massaging bubbles could bring on a terrific climax in a short time if I positioned myself just right. And this would frequently occur before I was completely erect.

"As soon as possible I experimented with T.R.H.'s technique. However, I made certain modifications which worked out very well. I did not remove the shower head. I have a pulsating massaging shower head which I usually keep on spray. By adjusting the head, I got three or four pulsating streams of water. Since I am uncut, I was able to pull the foreskin over the head of my cock, forming a small funnel into which I directed one of the streams. The water messaged the sensitive head of my cock but also seemed to stretch the foreskin, making a slight balloon effect. Of course this stimulation caused me to start getting hard, but before I was fully erect, I experienced a great climax. The only problem this caused was that the relaxed, satiated feeling was not a good way to start a professionally productive day. Since the first time, I have allowed the water to bring about an erection that lasts for 20 or 30 minutes and is stimulating but not debilitating. It's a fine way to start a day!"

I wasn't surprised to discover that, when these comments were discussed at an editorial meeting, we all had stories to tell. One of us designed and had his plumber build a facility with two shower heads, one in the usual position and the other just below the crotch. With the switch of a lever, the water could be diverted to the lower head or directed from both nozzles.

The intrepid editor of *CELEBRATE The Self*, Allen Erich, told this story: "I was a regular member of a health club until it went out of business. It had a men-only whirlpool, and I found that if I positioned myself properly, one of the water jets really worked over my penis, driving it from flaccid to erect in about thirty seconds and from erect or orgasmic in another minute. The bubbles were so prolific that my genitals were invisible, so I really got off letting the jet do its thing while I casually conversed with other men all around me. Of course there were times when I lost my train of thought, others when I had to bury my forehead in my hand and close my eyes and try to keep my breathing shallow. Occasionally I had to explain that I had low blood pressure, and the hot water didn't do it any good. Fortunately, no one asked why, if my blood pressure was low, my face had turned bright red.

"If any of my fellow club members are reading these words, I do apologize for any remnants of semen you naively carried home to your wives on various parts of your body."

My own water toy is much more prosaic, a clear plastic tube one and an eighth inches in diameter which, with some brute force, fits tightly into one of the five outlets in my jacuzzi tub. I can point it anywhere I like, usually beneath the shaft and into the scrotum where the tugging backward quickly leads to orgasm.

I also have a hand shower which I can use for direct stimulation on the upper part of the shaft.

Playing With Your Food

It's not easy to know where lotions end and toys begin. For example, how would you categorize the avocado? One enterprising fellow explains how he removes the pit from the avocado without splitting the fruit, warms the pulp in the microwave, and proceeds to copulate with it. As the avocado slides back and forth along his phallus, is it a lotion, a toy—or a gourmet delicacy?

Melons are a continuing favorite, particularly cantaloupe. Some men enjoy smearing their genitals in berries, particularly frozen blueberries. (Although I can't identify with this, I certainly applaud the creativity involved.)

Even eggplants might hold some interest, but not as a dildo. In *The Joy of Solo Sex*, I warned against indiscriminately inserting objects into the rectum. That warning wasn't heeded, apparently, by a man whose letter was published in the January, 1993, issue of *TantraMan*. He wrote: "In my endeavor to dilate the anal sphincter as much as possible, and as fast as possible, I incorporated the use of a rather large vegetable, an eggplant (snigger, snigger) for that purpose. And I lost it. In my ass. And couldn't get it out. How many times have you heard that one before! A friend of mine has forever been losing large objects up his ass, and I had vowed that it would never happen to me. Never say never, right?

"What it meant was a trip to Emergency. When the doctor couldn't get the offending thing out of my butt, it meant being prepped for surgery. I instructed the doctor that he most probably would not have to cut on me, but simply dilate my ass, reach in, and pull the object out.

"That is basically what he did. But it also bruised the shit out of my bladder and prostate, which caused it to swell enough to shut off my urethra. That meant a catheter. The whole miserable experience meant an extremely sore ass, asshole, bladder, urinary tract and two days in the hospital so that the swelling could go down.... I never want to eat or even buy another eggplant as long as I live."

Toys, as every child knows, can be used in common everyday ways—or they can be props in elaborate fantasies and games. In the next chapter, we'll show how some of the toys we've already discussed as well as others can be linked through the imagination with pleasurable and sometimes bizarre activities.

Chapter Five

Advanced Games
and Rich Men's Toys

When I was a kid growing up in Newark, New Jersey, I couldn't understand how anyone could eat roasted marshmallows. They were gooey, sickeningly sweet, and usually burned. By the time I was eighteen and counseling in a summer camp in the Poconos, I not only loved roasted marshmallows but had developed the knack for toasting them golden brown instead of coal black. Today, my only interest in roasted marshmallows is to smear them on my genitals and have others lick them off.

All of which goes to illustrate that our tastes change over the years. And, because sex expresses so many aspects of our personalities—power, generosity, gregariousness, worship/submission, our need for orgasm, physical closeness, sense of worth, escape from stress, and so much more—considering all those variables, anyone whose sexual fantasies, activities, and preferences don't change at all over a lifetime is a psychiatric phenomenon. In fact, he might well be embalmed.

To the creative imagination, those activities which we crowd under the general rubric of Sex are like items on a toy store's shelves. Scores and scores of different gadgets, all designed to bring joy in different ways. So it is with the true connoisseur of sex. Everywhere he looks, it seems, he finds objects which seem virtually designed with erotic purposes in mind. And, just as we would never think of telling a child with an electric train that he has no right to want a bicycle as well, we have no right to argue, "You have your wife's vagina or your husband's penis to play with; that should be enough."

Except for the brain dead, it is not enough. In this chapter, I am going to give you some of the more sophisticated lengths to which men have gone to entertain themselves sexually. This chapter is divided into two parts: Advanced Games and Rich Men Toys.

Advanced Games

Autointercourse

Let me state at the outset that some of these games can be dangerous, and *I am therefore not recommending those that are potentially harmful*. And if you are the squeamish type, and find things like bleeding and hanging distinctly unerotic, I suggest you skip this section.

Most of us have been advised at one time or another to "go fuck yourself!" At least some men can honestly respond, "Okay, I'll give it a try. Thanks."

D.N., of Hanover, Indiana, says:

I have always loved playing with my cock since I was very young. Recently I discovered a great new way of getting off. First let me say that I am not gay and have never been attracted to another man, though the thought of sucking a big engorged long cock has gotten me off many times. So I guess you could say that I am bi.

Anyway, I believe that when you get down to it there really isn't very much difference between men and women.

When I get myself off, just before I come I like the feeling of my ass being played with. Since the time I was little I would experiment with different objects inserted up my ass. Fingers, small bottles, etc. Now I have a new way:

I was in bed with my wife and we were holding each other. She was getting pretty aggressive and grabbed my cock real tight and pulled. She loves doing this and wants to rip it off, she gets so excited. She was bending my cock back and forth making it harder and harder. We were talking dirty as we sometimes do in the heat of passion. She grabbed me hard again and said, "I want to—Grr," while she yanked on my now throbbing cock.

I asked her what she wanted, or was thinking when she gritted her teeth. She wouldn't answer. She finally admitted that she wished she had a big cock just like mine that she could fuck me with. I kissed her passionately and shoved my fingers deeper in her pussy.

I then got an idea—with all the bending she was doing to my cock I said, "I bet you could fuck me with my cock!" She just looked at me with wide eyes, so I grabbed my cock and gently twisted it around me and then back so that it was facing towards my ass. It feels real good, if you are careful, to have a nice warm cock between your buns. Just the feel of the different temperatures is a turn on.

I then, with my wife's help, bent my cock so that about two to three inches were inside my own ass! I must tell you it is a great feeling, and it doesn't hurt—remember it's *your* cock! I then was able to fuck myself with my wife moving my cock in and out, and me keeping it bent back and my other hand to keep the head from popping out.

To feel your cock throb when you are getting ready to come really brings on an orgasm!

If you are interested in trying this, wait till your cock is soft or semi-hard rather than trying to bend it fully erect. You could strain yourself! When bending it back, first gently twist it ¼ to ½ turn as close to the base as possible, then spread your legs. I usually like doing this lying down on my back with my knees bent so I can raise myself up easily. Another way that has some added benefits is to use a chair—this helps in that you can more or less rotate back and forth on one bun to let your cock go in and out by sitting on it. Either way, when bending it back go around one side of your balls, not between them. I imagine that anyone with a cock around seven inches in length could get at least part in their ass. Mine is closer to nine inches, but the longer I get also makes it harder to keep from popping out.

This sounds like the ultimate in solo sex, even if you *do* have a partner. But I do want to caution you that the medical literature reports that, rarely, a rupture can occur in one or both of the sponge-like columns that expand with blood to create erections when the penis is severely twisted. It can also happen through a freak accident—say, awakening from an erotic dream, rushing to the bathroom in the dark and crashing dick-first into the sink. Usually, it's our zany, lovable, endless search for the newest sex kick that leads to disaster. The latest example I have heard about personally: A man in his mid-twenties suspended a five-pound weight from the tip of his erect penis by means of a shoe lace. His erection was actually rigid enough to support the weight. He even swung the weight forward and backward between his legs with no ill effects. Then, an excessively violent forward swing hurled the weight into free space. When it fell, it took up the slack with great force. The victim actually heard the "crack."

As the blood spilled from a corpus cavernosum into the surrounding tissue, his penis turned black-and-blue and enlarged to about four times its normal size. Within hours he was in surgery. The point: Be gentle with your little friend—he's all you've got.

Depilation

Perhaps it doesn't do anything for you, but *hair removal* turns some men on and even gets them off.

Says an Italian truck driver from New York City, "I'm hairy as an ape all over—chest, butt, back, legs. It's me. Do I like it? No. It's like my cock and balls used to be lost in all that hair around my privates, you know. So I went to this hair removal guy, and it cost me close to a thousand dollars, but now, when I drop my pants, you can count the pores on my dick and balls. It's a spotlight, all that skin surrounded by hair, and makes people stare. And of course that makes me get hard."

According to a recent issue of *Naturally*, a leading nudist publication, more and more men and women are showing up at nudist resorts minus genital hair. Practitioners say it makes them feel, well—more *naked*. Observers say it *looks* more naked. It obviously feels sexy as well, and some people undergo depilation (hair removal) not to be seen, but just for that reason—to feel sexy, and the process of removing the hair can even lead to orgasm.

"Just the anticipation gets me hot," writes a twenty-two year-old California man. "I stand there at the bathroom sink, my cock hanging across the marble counter, the razor poised. I'm actually gasping for breath. Maybe it's the symbolism, some masochistic ritual of genital sacrifice. I don't know what it is, but my heart is pounding, the dick spasming with each beat of my heart.

"I smear the shaving cream all over my pubic hair and down the rod, and around the balls, and then I stroke with the grain, or otherwise I end up with these little bleeding, painful nicks. Soon, there's nothing but skin above and to the sides of my dick. I start tugging on it, slowly, gently, while putting my foot up on the sink counter and letting my balls hang down so I shake and shave them. I watch myself in the mirror, big balls hanging, razor sliding smoothly over them, cock being manipulated, back and forth. I could come any time now, but I don't. I slow down, even stop, because I want to see those naked, hairless balls lying on the counter. I want to see this big, smooth, hair-naked dick get pounded off.

"And that's how it ends. I wash away all the shaving cream, wrap two hands around it, and watch that big, hairless dick blow its load."

If this sounds like something you'd like to try, here's what you need to know about dipilation:

There are three popular methods of professional hair removal in use today. The "tweezer" method consists of a small clamp that holds a half dozen or so hairs at one time while an electrical charge of two or three seconds is applied. There is no pain at this point. However, when the process is over the hairs have to be pulled out one by one, and this may cause some pain. (The hair can be removed by waxing, which is faster, but there is still a little pain involved.)

The second and third methods both involve inserting a fine probe into the hair follicle. The second method uses multiple sterile needles (sixteen in all) that, once inserted along the hair follicle, are left for approximately five minutes while electric current is applied.

The third technique is the "blend" method, so named because it combines direct and alternating current that causes a chemical change in the tissue. It is done with a single probe (sterile disposable needle) inserted into the hair follicle, but the amount of time is from five to ten seconds and the hair is removed immediately. With this method an electrologist can remove from 200 to 600 hairs in an hour, depending on the structure of the hair and the depth of the hair follicle. This is considered to be the most effective method. There is a slight sting when the current is applied, but you soon get used to it.

Electrologists who use the "tweezer" method swear by it, but all others say that it is not permanent, primarily because it does not use a needle that can effectively kill the hair follicle.

Regardless of the method used, plan on at least three sessions in order to achieve anything close to permanent removal.

Cost is another factor. You will find electrologists listed in the Yellow Pages under "Electrology" or "Electrolysis." Call all who are listed, both for price and to find out whether or not they will do pubic hair, if that is what you are interested in, because many do not, especially men's pubic hair. Also check those in a neighboring community or city. Prices vary. The average is from $45 to $60 for a one-hour session. With the second method, you also have to pay for the multiple needles. No doubt they will be yours to keep once you are finished.

Of course if you're just in it for the kicks and want to do it for yourself, there are, in addition to the razor, effective and painless hair removal ointments. You'll find them in any pharmacy.

Sounds

In my late twenties, while bathing, I discovered a long, thin artist's paintbrush drying on the sink, and, predictably, immediately put it to erotic use, inserting the entire ten or twelve inches into my urethra. Two days later, unable to urinate, I rushed to a local hospital emergency room to be catheterized. A gush of fresh blood preceded a bladder full of urine. I had suffered a severe bladder infection, was hospitalized for four days, faced the possibility of surgery if the antibiotics hadn't worked, and struck up an affair with a lovely nurse who took pity on a poor slob who had nothing but paintbrushes to make out with—so I told her.

Actually, many—perhaps most—men at one time or another have inserted objects into their urethras. In fact, some objects, called "sounds," have been designed specifically for the purpose. These medical devices are made of metal and used to break up fibrous blockages, or "strictures," in the urethra or to crush bladder stones. Richard P. gave me a fascinating report on the use of sounds:

> A friend of mine once demonstrated for me how he could feed his flaccid dick onto a ¼-inch threaded 10"-long bolt, up through his urethra, and not even flinch, but rather, convulse out a load around it. (Don't try this at home alone! In fact, don't try it *at all!*)
>
> After this heroic demonstration, I had from then on held to the idea of filling my own cock—not with a threaded bolt, but something far more gentle, mostly just to experience the feeling of fullness. I began experimenting with an oral thermometer, which gave me a good reading but *no* feeling at all, and besides I was

afraid I would push it in too far and lose it and then what? Later I came across a nice glass cocktail stirrer with a balled end, but after one try I prudently decided against anything breakable.

I graduated to a plastic knitting needle after I had rounded off the pointed end. This was better, but still way too thin for giving me the fully stuffed feeling I had hoped for. The solution came form an unlikely source: I purchased for my antique shop some old medical tools, including several metal rods of various shapes and sizes which an M.D. friend described as "sounds." As soon as I knew what they were, I began preparations for sterilizing a long unbreakable steel sound for penetration into my own urethra channel, a device specifically designed for this very purpose.

I was *hot* with anticipation and my dick was in its drooling, rock-hard state. I did a thorough polishing and sterilization of a choice sound that looked long enough to slide up at least to my prostate, and seemed to be of an acceptable diameter, with a gently swollen protuberance around the shaft about four inches from the tip which increased the diameter at this point to perhaps half an inch. It also had a gentle curve beginning about two inches from the rounded tip end.

With free-flowing pre-cum drooling for lubrication, I began to push it into my piss slit and on up into my urethra channel, but not far. I painfully discovered that you can't slide a curved sound into a rock-hard straight cock.

After I had grown somewhat accustomed to the self-messaging feeling of having a good ol' steel reinforced dick and pressurized prostate, I began to move my body a little, at first very cautiously, then gradually I began almost involuntarily to hump the air and just let the sound swing up and down quite forcefully so that with every downward swing it would press deeply into my prostate and give me a real nice "getting there" sensation.

And getting there I was! I was actually jacking my prostate. My pre-cum began to slobber out from around the inserted sound and now with my left hand I held onto my steel stuffed cock and with my right began to move the sound ever so gently up and down and around inside my urethra. The little molded protuberance felt really sweet as it slipped up and down ever so slightly giving my urethra lining the just right sort of extra massage so as to feel wildly stimulating. About twenty seconds of this and I was shooting my first steel-packed load. It oozed out and around the sound and with each ejac the slight discomfort increased, but there was no stopping it now, so I really milked myself out a good one by more aggressively moving my hard shaft up and down around the sound as much as I could and also moving the sound itself up and down and around.

This is where the curve of the sound really comes into play, and when the contractions finally stopped after that very first sound "get off," I just let my exhausted but over-stimulated dick hang there and convulse itself down to flaccidity.

I had to get rid of the tumescence completely before I could extract the sound, so with my spent cock hanging vertically, head downwards in total submission with the weight of the sound, so sorrowfully sad looking, the sound suddenly shot out and clanged onto the slate floor, but the curve of the sound as it speedily exited really roughed up my urethra. I learned fast: always remove the sound from your urethra channel gently.

That initial sound-packed "get off" began an addiction—but I had a few mishaps about which I must forewarn you. Never, I mean *never*, pack a sound into your urethra without being absolutely sure it is 200 percent sterile. I once got hasty, trying to show off for a kinky voyeur. (Which reminds me, in my collection were several double-ended sounds which could be used for two insertions at the same time; I've never done that, but I have it in mind.)

Anyhow, for my demonstration I used one which I had sterilized several sessions earlier but which had somehow become septic in storage. Even though I had packed it away in sterile gauze, a few days later I developed the worst bladder infection imaginable. Fever, chills, weakness and every other discomfort. Finally after a confession to my urologist, who allowed that such insertions are not all that uncommon but didn't exactly give me his blessings either, I received an antibiotic and was cured. Should you ever start with sounds, always, always be overly assiduous about sterilization.

There is a proper medical way to lubricate and prepare the urethra for insertions, which I have never gotten the equipment to do for myself, and that is to first lubricate the urethra with a medical Irrigation Syringe filled with a water soluble Medial Anti-Bacterial Lubricant, said to be an interesting sensation all its own.

One other thing that I didn't expect but happened was, once when I was using a very small diameter sound, mostly just to see how something way too small would feel, I let it hang there as I customarily did with my usual larger one, but when I started my simulated humping, within seconds several drops of blood began to seep out around the insertion along with the usual pre-cum. It seems that the small size allowed the tip end to press too deeply into the urethra somewhere on the way up.

Well, this scared me half to death, and that made for a record fast trip from tumescence to flaccidity, but after it was all over and after a good post-insertion piss, there was no more blood or later complications.

Also, after you shoot a load and take your first post-orgasmic piss there will most likely be a fiery burning sensation all up and down your urethra. For a few real masochists I have spoken with, this burning is, to them, a really sought-for condition. Personally I hated it when it used to occur in my early days of dick stuffing. I have finally determined that this was probably caused by the added pressure as the cum is ejaculated out around the sound. This burning seems to finally disappear after several good orgasmic sessions. Perhaps the urethra has been toughened enough so that the added force of those super powerful ejaculations are no longer troublesome.

If you can't find any old sounds, new ones are available by mail from Desmodus, Inc. Quite expensive, but they are stainless and new and individually packaged and sterile. Desmodus also sells a 60cc Piston Irrigation Syringe as well as the proper Sterile Lubricant for injection. Regarding size, as I recall I began with a one-quarter inch diameter and am now up to a five-eighths inch and ready for the next step up. I suppose my current HOT fantasy is to be able to finger fuck my own dick! With a condom, for sure! How's that for the ultimate safe, hot, solo get off?

The most stuffed penis that I have ever known hangs from the groin of a Mr. Jack C. of Canada. In 1993, he wrote to me saying, "Jacking off so frequently over 30 years has led me to explore novel ways of self-pleasure. My cock and balls have become a focus for daring feats of physical play: the exploration leading me ultimately to cock *insertion* rituals that get me super hot. I must confess that it is purely because my eager cum tube oozes forth so much pre-cum that my tract is lubricated for such acts of penetration.

"When I get into stroking myself, the clear, slick juices just bubble out my cock slit, inviting me to feed objects down inside. I own a 10-inch Kodak darkroom thermometer that was my first 'toy,' which I still love to plunge all the way into my urethra for an opening warm-up. The smooth glass rod glides in and out of my cock as I ream my organ ecstatically. More recently I have begun to utilize a smooth 3/8″-thick stainless steel rod almost a foot in length.

"When the breach is fully prepared, lubricant flowing freely, then I am ready to be fed the 'ammo'—steel ball-bearings! One by one the heavy orbs are inserted into my gaping slit, descending in a clatter down my cum-tube as I feed up to 40 3/8″ bearings at once into my throbbing member. The sensation of the dense row of metal all the way down past the base of my cock is so wild. In a sensational finale, I bring myself off, shooting a barrage of shiny steel and creamy cum into the air.

"This sensational ritual has become a hallmark of my jack-off career."

Although it has nothing to do with insertions, I think you'll find interesting the remainder of Jack's letter. It has to do with another sex toy—Jack's own semen. His "obsession," as he calls it, is not at all unusual.

"After years of spewing my ejaculate randomly, my fascination for such spurting volleys of jizz has intensified. Gradually they become ritualistic, the urge to sample my prize load surfacing as a deep desire. Licking my ejaculate up off the mirror became a new passion. Before long, I was practicing yoga, legs kicked back over my head, jerking my dick straight into my open mouth.

"I am addicted to cum—my own cum! For the past six years or so I have been shooting off into my lips regularly. Inspired by performing on video, these passionate sessions elicit the beast within, eating each eruption with unfaltering dedication. The unique taste of my semen fills my senses throughout the day as I secretly drink each burst I elicit. Casually, at home, or under the table at a restaurant. Beat it...Eat it!"

Piercing

Twenty years ago, genital piercing was an esoteric practice enjoyed by a few, and unheard of—let's face it, unimagined— even by most connoisseurs of kinky sex. Then, in October of 1977, Jim Ward, of Gauntlet Enterprises in Los Angeles, published volume one, issue one, of *Piercing Fans International Quarterly*—or *PFIQ*. I own two copies of that first issue and my collection is complete up to number thirty-three, published in 1989. It's still being published, but, at forty dollars a year, it's a bit too rich for my blood. More recent issues are filled with photographs, many in color, of both males and females pierced in every part of their anatomies. The phallus of the man named John, featured in number thirty-two, boasts one hundred eighty piercings. There are so many chrome-beaded bars through his dick that one can hardly see flesh.

Since those early days when *PFIQ* was first published, body piercing has become mainstream, with the genitals becoming one of the more popular impaling targets. One reason for its popularity, I imagine, is the same as for any other new fad in appearance or dress: it's a legal but obvious way to tell the establishment to go to hell. Spiked hair, shaved heads and steel bars through the nose, cheek, and tongue aren't beautiful. They may even be ugly. But they do proclaim, in startling fashion, "This is my hair/nose/cheek/tongue, and nobody's going to tell me what I can and can't do with it."

But when it comes to genital piercing, the motive is different. Some people claim that the piercing sensitizes the organ, whether nipple, scrotum, perineum, glans, labia, or clitoris. More likely, the increased sensitivity is psychological; what the piercing does is make one acutely aware at all times of one's genitals, and that heightened awareness creates a chronic sexual arousal.

That continual titillation is the goal of one type of piercing, which I call long-term, or decorative piercing. N.K., of New Jersey, writes at length about his experiences with long-term piercings:

> I continued modeling nude after college, and only "semi-retired" from modeling this past year to pursue a long-time interest of mine, body piercing, specifically penis piercing. Though this had interested me for many years, it was only recently, when piercing became so popular and piercing services were readily available, that I was able to turn this interest into reality. I had my first cock-piercing performed in July of last year, two foreskin piercings, one on each side of my foreskin, and the third piercing through my frenum. The piercings are 10 gauge, leaving a hole slightly larger than 1/10 inch in diameter, and I wear a 5/8 inch diameter stainless steel ring in each of these piercings. The foreskin piercings were quite painless—the sensation was as if my foreskin had been pinched. The frenum piercing was more uncomfortable, perhaps because I'm extremely sensitive in that area of my penis, and being "prepped" for the piercing—having my frenum swabbed with a surgical scrub and stretched for the marking of the piercing—

brought on the start of an erection and my cock became totally erect just as the needle penetrated my frenum. I am not a masochist by any means, but I felt that I was very close to inadvertently coming as my frenum was pierced.

I did need to wait two days before resuming masturbating and then did it very gently. One of the benefits of piercing is that it noticeably increased the sensitivity of the pierced area, and I was totally amazed by the heightened sensitivity I felt, particularly in my frenum as I worked my foreskin. I had an exceptionally intense come and a very heavy discharge, with more ejaculations than usual. After the two-month healing period, I found that I could get myself off very pleasantly by using my frenum ring to stimulate the frenum, alternately stretching it and relaxing it, letting the sensation there build up until a final pull on the ring triggers my orgasm.

I began considering a fourth piercing, this for my cock-head. A standard Prince Albert would not be suitable for me, not only because of my frenum piercing, but also because my pee-hole slit is larger than average and actually extends into my frenum, literally splitting my head in two on the underside. I decided on a reverse Prince Albert, where the piercing is performed through the top of the cock-head and the ring passes through the top of the head, into the urethra, and out the pee-hole. I had this done in November and it was quite an erotic experience. It was also far less uncomfortable than my frenum piercing, a pleasant surprise for me.

The "prepping" was interesting. A cotton swab was dipped in surgical scrub, inserted into my pee-hole, and up my urethra to prep the head internally, then the surgical scrub was applied to the top of the

head, and the location of the piercing was measured and marked. My pee-hole was spread open and a stainless steel tube was inserted into my urethra to receive the piercing needle. The needle was passed through my cock-head and into the tube, the tube was withdrawn, and the needle used to guide the ring through my head and out my slit, then the bead was snapped into the ring to close it, completing the piercing. This is a 10 gauge stainless steel ring, one-inch in diameter, although the pierced hole in my cock-head is oversized, 6 gauge, to facilitate insertion of the ring.

After the piercing, I waited six days before resuming masturbating, but it was well worth the wait, as the sensations I felt were indescribably erotic, and my come was even more intense and satisfying. I have since discovered that rotating the ring to pass the bead into my pee-hole and leaving it inside my urethra provides a constant pleasurable sensation and also increases the pleasure of masturbating. I have no hesitation in recommending penis piercings for anyone who enjoys solo sex. It's worth mentioning that "dydoe" piercings is done through the rim of the cock-head and short ball-tipped studs inserted through the rim. There are typically two of these piercings, one on each side of the rim, and they restore some of the sensitivity lost because of the removal of the protective foreskin.

In contrast to long-term piercers, those whom I term recreational piercers seek the impaling of genital flesh not as a means to an end but an end in itself. To my knowledge, this distinction hasn't been made before, but its an important one if for no other reason than that it helps the self-piercer understand precisely what brings him joy so that he might seek it out more directly.

"There were two parts to the ritual," says a young executive editor with a major publishing company. "First was the feeling, a kind of tingling, when I pushed the needle through the head of my dick. Perhaps I should say there were three things. The feeling was one. Then there was the visual, my helpless, erect penis forced tight against the sink, held motionless by my thumb, elastic bands keeping the blood in it so it was so red it was almost purple, the skin so tight it was ready to rupture, and this needle slowly disappearing into it, in one side, through the urethra, out the other. I would tremble I was so excited, like someone with Parkinson's or something. I would be gasping. I couldn't take my eyes off it. And then the third thing. I'd pull the needle out quickly and there would be blood shooting out both sides, pouring out the urethra. It seemed like gallons of it, but it was never more than a quarter of a cup. It was like my cock had been slaughtered. Sometimes I would just ejaculate without even doing anything.

"The whole thing was so overwhelming, I would just collapse on the floor later. The erection would go down and the bleeding would stop immediately, and I'd fall asleep just exhausted and really, really satisfied."

I had a personal interview with this man, and he joked that it's a real bitch to clean up afterward, and he finally lost interest in the practice, but he remains puzzled about why the act of "slaughtering" his penis was more overwhelmingly pleasurable than any other sexual experience of his life. There are any number of answers. The most obvious is sexual shame instilled in him as a child. He can enjoy sex only after he has been punished, so that by first destroying the source of his pleasure, he is free to abandon himself to orgasm. That was Theodore Reik's explanation for masochism.

Or, he may have a violent, sadistic impulse. Unconsciously, he may wish to destroy another man's phallus, and acting out that fantasy with himself as his own victim was sexually satisfying.

I believe that it's important for each of us to know what makes us tick, both sexually and otherwise. Not so that we can change who we are—not at all. Because psychotherapy is a profit-making industry, the emphasis in dealing with eccentricities and deviations from the norm has been much too often on making people become carbon copies of each other. That would lead not only to an intolerably monotonous world, but it would require people to play roles that are neither normal nor right for them. Our goals, as individuals and as sex therapists and psychotherapists, ought to be to help others:

—Find out who they really are;

—Help them to accept, appreciate, and even celebrate themselves;

—Show them how to function legally and successfully in the real world.

I have a case in point—controversial, certainly, but a perfect example. Following publication of *The Joy of Solo Sex*, I received a letter mailed from Arlington, Texas. Its author confessed that he had been a pedophile for thirty-five years, had been jailed several times, had undergone every conceivable treatment with no success. Back on the streets after ten years behind bars, he had been attracted to a young teenaged boy. Instead of approaching the youth, he went to a bookstore, hoping to find some material on children.

He left with a copy of my book, and was particularly taken with the section entitled *Fantasy Is More Real*. He read it again and again, practicing the techniques for envisioning through all the senses.

He wrote, "Once I realized that I could have anyone I wanted in bed with me any time of the day or night, my life changed. I mean, I can really *have* that person there. Every smell and touch and everything. And it's not against the law. I think I found the answer, and I won't be going back behind bars, thanks to your book."

In my opinion, recreational piercing can be fun for some, and even therapeutic.

Rich Men's Toys

Vacuum Pumps

I've been using various vacuum pumps for a couple of decades now, and, depending on the quality of the gadget in question, I've found them 1) a really hot deviation from the boring routine of workaday sex; 2) a pleasant enough diversion; 3) as frustrating as hell because a) the base doesn't fit tightly enough against the groin to create a vacuum; b) the hose pops off the pump or tube just because, in your frenzy, you begin thrashing while pumping; c) the piece of junk they call a pump just—breaks!

If you want to buy a reasonably priced manual pump, here's what it will do for you:

It will help you get an erection. (Because the vacuum that's created actually sucks the penis into engorgement, it would help a *dead* man to get an erection.) If you place a non-strangulating elastic band around the base of your penis far enough forward not to interfere with the latex that presses against your groin, you can then remove the pump and maintain the erection if you have trouble doing so under ordinary circumstances.

Incidentally, one of the best materials for making elastic cock rings of various sizes is a bicycle tire inner tube. If the fit is too tight at first, cut a thinner one and stretch it on a broom handle overnight.

These pumps will also transform dinky dicks into Mammoth Monsters. If you've never used a pump before, you'll be awed at the sight of your own equipment after leaving the pump in place for ten minutes at a suction just short of uncomfortable. (Never leave the pump on for more than 15 minutes or tissue can be damaged.) You'll look like John Holmes—

only alive—and just looking at yourself can be a powerful aph-
rodisiac.

It's important to know how this enlargement happens: the
cells that form the tissue of your penis expand into the surrounding vacuum and become filled with blood and other liquid. If the vacuum is too severe, the tissue walls can rupture,
causing bleeding beneath the skin (bruising), and in some cases
little beads of blood on the glans.

If this extreme suction continues too long, you'll end up
with a purple prick, and it will take a week or two for that
blood beneath the skin to be reabsorbed. This is not a smart
move, since cells are literally being torn apart.

Here are some things that vacuum pumps *can't* do. They
cannot lead to permanent enlargement. Claims to the contrary
are either unknowingly misleading or deliberately deceiving. As
soon as the vacuum of the pump is released, the excess liquid
in the cells begins to slowly seep through the cell walls and
back into the blood stream. Unless the cells are so severely
damaged that they've lost their elasticity, they won't remain
enlarged for more than a few hours after the vacuum is gone.

Vacuum pumps will not enlarge the balls, although they
can temporarily stretch the skin of the scrotum and suck fluid
into the sac, swelling it. More importantly, too much vacuum
suction on the scrotum can cause varicocele and hemorrhage in
the complex network of arteries and veins supplying the testes.

As for electric pumps, some come with nipple-enlarging
attachments (for $49 extra). The basic costs are $270, and
additional cylinders are another $59. Assuming you buy the
whole package, you'll be shelling out $380 plus tax.

Not everyone is happy with electric vacuum pumps, however, even if the price doesn't get the better of them. One *CSN*
subscriber writes, "I sprang for the Vacu Tech system a couple
of years ago and decided it was a bit too much for me. It
sucked one of my testicles into the vacuum tube and, after I
pushed the release switch the wrong way, it actually increased
the vacuum. There aren't many worse feelings than having

your favorite parts in jeopardy and feeling helpless to rescue them. I looked on in panic-stricken horror as my greatly swollen cock resisted all efforts to dislodge the vacuum tube and my testicle weighed in with its own feelings of imminent doom.

"All I could think was, 'What have I done to you guys!' I promised that if 'we' ever got out of this, I would treat them right all afternoon. In one adrenaline-driven power surge, I managed to yank the tube loose.

"As I sat on the floor in a cold sweat, lungs heaving, I gently manipulated my bruised testicle and massaged my still very swollen and sullen-looking member. The cool air blowing over my penis never felt so good. As things began to settle back down, I had to live with a gnawing fear that perhaps I had done something serious to that testicle. It was letting me know that the encounter had not gone well. After some time, when it appeared that no harm was done, I tried it again (more carefully) and had some enjoyment going around the house doing chores with my cock stuck up red and hard in the disconnected vacuum tube.

"But that was it. I thought the vacuum might induce orgasmic feelings, but it did not, and I was informed by Vacu Tech this was never the intended use. Since I am not into serious cock enlargement through suction (I don't believe it works; the only guy who comes out with a huge dong is he who went in with one), and not wishing to jeopardize an erection system that works very well unassisted, I dropped the Vacu Tech 'program.'"

Top of the line Solo Sex machines

The Venus II Ejaculator

Now that the Accu-Jac is no more, there's an obvious demand for a machine that will do all the work and free both hands to hold magazines and turn pages, caress other parts of their anatomy, wave to the neighbors or whatever. The Venus II is one effort to meet that demand.

93

To begin, I'm satisfied that the 3S Corporation, which manufactures the Venus II, is honest and reliable. The gadget does what it's advertised to do, and it's ruggedly constructed. While suspended between a hassock and a sofa, I began thrusting with such violence that I pulled the machine off the sofa. The crash thereof was great, but the machine whacked away without missing a beat, albeit scaring the spunk out of me.

Specifically, the sleeve slides up and down on the penis. It seems particularly useful in converting a flaccid phallus to a randy rod much more quickly than a human hand might. True, it takes time and tinkering to master—as does a BMW. One must adjust the length of the stroke to one's preference, along with the pressure. (One tester complained that the sleeve kept flying off his penis, but the problem was solved through a minor adjustment.)

Among our testers, the uncircumcised gentleman would have preferred a much looser sleeve, and even then the machine might not prove satisfactory. Regardless of all the silly propaganda, the fact is that an uncircumcised glans is more sensitive, all things being equal, than its circumcised counterpart. Although a circumcised tester needed relentless stimulation over several minutes to bring him to orgasm, the uncircumcised tester's penis became painfully sensitive. He had to abort the flight before takeoff two out of three times.

3S offers a 45-day, $75.00 trial offer. If the buyer isn't completely satisfied, he can call for a return authorization number within month and a half, and the purchase price will be refunded less $75.00. The customer gets to keep the sleeve, which is valued at $35.00.

He also gets to view (although he must return) the $19.95 training video.

Would I buy it? No. Not at $1,095.00. Even with the occasional discount that the company offers of $126.00, the price is still $969.00. I asked two of our testers what they thought.

The first said, "I'd buy it in a snap at $350.00. At a thousand dollars I'll just have to keep doing it myself."

Said the other, "If I were impotent, or if I had arthritis or some other handicap that made solo sex difficult or impossible, I'd buy the Venus II no matter what the cost. And if I had money to burn, yes, I'd buy it even if I had no handicaps. I don't have that kind of money, though."

My evaluation: an excellent machine, well built, that does what it claims—but much too expensive. If you want to take a test flight of your own, write to 3S Corporation of America, 830-11 Seton Court, Wheeling, Illinois 60090-5772. Or, you can call 708-808-0732. You'll have to supply a check or credit card number for the entire amount before the machine can be shipped, but it won't be charged to your account until after the 45-day trial period is up.

The Motorized Orgasmic Release Device

Unlike the Venus II, the MOR works not on a vacuum system but a mechanical motion principle that slides a cup back and forth on the penis. This can give a sensation quite similar to being masturbated by a human being. It is also the same approach that I described in the very first issue of CSN when I talked about the first masturbation machine I invented:

"[It] utilized a 120-volt electric motor which turned a wheel which thrust a levered rod up and down. At the end of the rod was attached a metal ring into which the penis was inserted. The first time I tested it, the stroke was too radical. The down-stroke stunningly bashed my nuts, and the up-stroke nearly ripped the head off my dick."

The action of the MOR is not up and down but in and out, and the speed is controlled, and, in place of the metal ring (ouch!) is a plastic cup. (Several sizes are included, so you're sure to find one loose or tight enough to fit your fancy.) Inside the cup are two removable membranes, amazingly soft and skin-like. These, too, are supplied in various sizes.

The cup is attached to a tube with a bulb on the end. The instructions advise lubricating the penis, squeezing the bulb to create a vacuum, then inserting your organ into the cup and releasing the bulb in order to create a snug fit. I found a better way—I removed the bulb, inserted my organ deep into the cup, forcing the air out through the now open end of the tube, squeezed the bulb tightly, attached it to the tube, and released the bulb. That created a very strong suction, even when the penis was flaccid.

The MOR was tested by two men, and the reactions were as different as sexual tastes can make them. Said tester #1, "I ran the machine on slow at first. The sensation was interesting, different, but not spectacular. I then increased the speed of the motor. Somehow my member was going forward (toward the machine) as the rod and cup were moving away from the machine and toward me. There was a minor collision and my erect member was bent to the side. There was no damage to myself, but I feel there could have been."

Tester #2 said, "You have to be totally passive with this machine—watch a video, read, fantasize. I sat with my back to the headboard, the machine between my legs, hooked myself up, turned it on and relaxed. It got me off just fine. (I fantasized that I was one of a dozen 'cows' held captive in a sperm farm, getting milked every hour on the hour.)

"The second time I used it, I suspended myself between a chair and bed, my organs hanging toward the floor. This was tricky. I had to position the gadget at an angle, supported by pillows. It took a while, but once I got it going, and got back into the sperm farm fantasy, it worked swell."

Clearly, what—or who—turns us on varies radically from one guy to another. Some of us like our sex laced with new, challenging adventure. Yet, one of our staff said, "I prefer to lube up and use my hand."

Like the Venus II, the MOR is over-priced at $865.00. If you'd like more information, write to the company at P.O. Box 1007, Malibu, CA 90265, or call (310) 456-9353.

Vibrators

I've saved vibrators for last because, if the truth be known, the only sex toy to which I return repeatedly and have for decades is a pistol-gripped vibrator and a cup (The Litten Cup) which I designed fifteen years ago for my own personal pleasure and have only recently begun manufacturing for others who are true connoisseurs of solo sex. One gentleman sings the praises of his vibrator as follows:

Touching the vibrator down my shaft and over the little ridge onto my sensitive glans sent chills through my body. With my free hand, I clutched my balls tightly to savor the vibrations.

Stopping to catch my breath, I grabbed a tube of KY jelly and smeared some on my penis. The lube felt pleasant and cooled my warm wand. I was ready to vibe off, in a different way.

Removing the towel from the sink, I laid my lubed cock on the smooth edge of the sink, I hunched over my cock with the Magic Wand again. This time, the head of the vibrator slid easily up and down my greased shaft.

The slippery vibrations were very potent and pleasing. The KY made my penis look slick and shiny. Each pass of the vibe smeared more lube over my shaft and made funny little squishy sounds.

I started thrusting my slippery cock in and out, between the smooth porcelain and the vibrator's soft foam head. My pelvis moved back and forth, in and out. The movements were awkward at first, until I found my rhythm. It felt so good, fucking the sink.

The slippery sensations were intense. I was throbbing, so hot and sweaty that my pubes glistened. I wanted to come. I needed to come. Then I had to cum! No turning back.

The orgasm was so strong it made me stand up on my toes. My inner sex muscles clenched and released jets of sperm, again and again. Opening my eyes, I glanced into the mirror in time to see my sperm spurting out.

The vibrator is my favorite sex toy and has rekindled my self-pleasuring. I have become an expert at coming using the vibrator, giving myself many orgasms. I use the vibe twice a day, once in the morning and evening.

I leave my vibrator at my bedside, plugged in and ready to go. Almost daily, my morning ritual is waking up by using my vibrator.

You want to avoid two potential problems when shopping for vibrators. The first is inadequate power. I have shelled out good money only to discover that the motor in the vibrator was not capable of shaking me as much as I wanted to be shaked— and, unfortunately, there is no labeling requirement to give you the motor's performance capabilities. But there are a few steps you can take that can help you buy wisely;

—If you can feel the weight of the vibrator, do so. Usually, the heavier the gadget the more powerful the motor.

—Buy brand names. The Sears pistol-grip vibrator, for example, will do the job.

—Read *Good Vibrations Guide to Sex* by Cathy Winks and Anne Semans. It's published by Cleis Press, and can be ordered through any bookstore.

Finally, there is the question of attachments. In all honesty, there isn't a single attachment on the market that I can recommend. In fact, the "Come-Cup" is the *only* attachment on the market that fits the pistol-grip vibrators as well as the penile glans. I've tested it, and find it inadequate for several reasons:

1) It isn't deep enough.

2) It isn't wide enough. That means that the intensity of the vibration and where it occurs can't be controlled. The

"lips" beat the hell out of the tip of the penis and give no vibration behind the glans.

3) Although I haven't proven it yet, there may be a chemical used in the manufacturing process of this attachment which irritates sensitive skin, especially among men with foreskins. On repeated occasions following the use of the "Come-Cup," an allergic rash resulted which was treated through cortisone ointment. There seemed to be no other factors in common except the use of the cup.

The Litten Cup is large enough to accept the entire glans. It fits tightly around the shaft while leaving the glans untouched—or it can be moved to provide contact with the corona only, or with the tip of the penis only. The organ can fit loosely, or be sucked through vacuum deep into the cup. If desired, the user can "wear"the cup and vibrator by allowing it to hang from the organ without support. For more information, write to Factor Press, PO Box 8888, Mobile, AL 36689.

Chapter Six

Sharing Solos

Solo sex has always been regarded as an also-ran sexual activity because it's considered a solitary pursuit. Apart from the fact that solitary activities are often the most profound and meaningful, most of us can testify from personal experience that solo sex is particularly delightful when it's shared.

That sharing begins for most of us at an early age. J.B., of Rochester, New York, writes:

> I began to masturbate alone at age 12, and soon discovered that my boyhood friend since birth also had discovered the joys of solo sex. At first we masturbated separately, then found higher excitement masturbating in front of each other, then even greater excitement at masturbating each other. As both our parents worked, we had our homes free until 6 P.M. every day.
>
> We would both strip completely naked, and get hard-ons by pretending to be sexually excited by

photos in girlie magazines. Later, we were honest about being really excited by each other.

Sometimes we stood up and slowly rubbed our erect cocks against each other until climax. Sometimes we manually rubbed our cocks together until our fingers, pubic hair, and balls were soaked with semen.

Of course, many times masturbation was skipped and we learned to have anal sex, and (our favorite) oral sex. We really regarded oral sex as masturbation of your cock by another boy's mouth—plus the extra excitement at watching your cock get sucked off, sometimes shooting the jizz all over his face, sometimes in his mouth, sometimes having it swallowed!

From ages 16-18 oral masturbation was our favorite, but a nice slow hand job was great, too! Masturbation and homo sex during the 20's was never as exciting as during our teens.

Another mans writes, "As far back as I can remember, I've enjoyed manipulating my foreskin. This led to my more or less accidental discovery of masturbation at some point between the ages of eight and nine, when a more prolonged exercising of my foreskin produced my first ejaculation. By the time I was nine years old, I was masturbating regularly with my friends, five other boys of my age or slightly older who had also discovered self-pleasure. In mild weather, we masturbated outdoors, behind a row of backyard garages, out of sight from the neighboring houses, and at other times, we masturbated in the basements of our homes. I was the only one in the group who was not circumcised, and my very "different" cock attracted a considerable amount of attention from my friends.

"Eventually we began experimenting with masturbating each other, and because of my "different" cock, I was a very popular choice for my friends to masturbate, and it was very exciting to look down and watch someone else's hand working my foreskin back and forth over my cock-head. It felt strange at first to masturbate my friends, with little or no foreskin to use, but it was nevertheless enjoyable to bring them to climax and hold their cocks as they ejaculated. By the time we were eleven, the group gradually broke up, though my best friend, Bobby, and I continued to masturbate together and to masturbate each other for another year or so until his family moved out of town. I can't recall how many times a day I climaxed then, but it was probably a rather high number, thanks to the stamina of youth. After coming several times with my friends, I'd go home and masturbate in the bathroom, and I don't think I ever took a shower in those days without stroking myself off."

Another correspondent, who insists that he isn't gay, says, "When I was a youngster, eight or nine years old, until about sixteen, solo was ninety-five percent of my sexual enjoyment. The other five percent was when I found someone to masturbate me, girl or boy. When it was a boy, I of course would reciprocate. Funny thing, it was better with another boy, or man, than with a girl, as far as masturbating goes. Maybe because the boy or man also had a penis, and he had better technique. It was fun playing with another boy's hard cock."

J.B., from Oklahoma, remembers playing an erotic game: "When I first began to cum, a friend and I had a race—from first touch to cum. Fourteen seconds was my record. He once did it in ten seconds, but I would bet he had been after it off and on all day.

"We were always scared to death an adult would catch us. It's no wonder we have so many psychotic people in the fifty-seventy age group, especially here in the so-called Bible Belt." (J.B. speculates about the number of ejaculations possible within a 24-hour period. Referring to his childhood, he says, "I believe my little brother once did eight in a row—but he is weird.")

There are at least three reasons that a solosexual would enjoy having a playmate:

—Lust, or sexual heat, is contagious. I know a man in his early fifties who never is able to get an erection until he arouses his partner into a rampant frenzy of sexual desire. Hearing the moans, seeing the abdomen heave in spasms of delight, fills him with sexual frenzy, as though a surplus of lust overflows from the other person and fills him up.

But there needn't be any contact. Two people can be driven wild simply by watching each other. That's the whole idea of the poem "Knight Watch" by Jerry, Champaign, IL:

> At first we only listened
> for the predictable furtive sound
> of moving covers
> and looked for confirmation
> to the middle of the other bed
> alive in shadows
> with little rustlings and catches of breath
>
> There was no need to say anything
> Mouths were silent as hands talked
> louder now
> in heated conversation with the self
> growing more and more urgent
>
> Gradually somehow the covers crept down
> to reveal more distinct and carnal sounds and shadows
> and deeper sighs
>
> Then one night we casually
> deliberately
> left a light on
> knowing why

One's glance turned from time to time
to the other
then away
so other glance could turn to him
alternate at first
discreet
avoiding the eyes
but soon
unchallenged
simultaneous
extended
open

Unstated unrestricted license given
we turned our heads toward each other's bed
urging with frank gazes
encouraging
admiring
showing our stuff
teaching our moves
together or in turns
one watching
waiting
twitching
while the other worked
listening to fleshy sounds
dry at first
growing moist and wetter
fascinated by the shared exposed and risen maleness

They were of a length

We looked and listened and felt
hunger heightened by the sense
of shared sensation
learning exquisite ways of self-enjoyment
from an expert close at hand
and no mere instructor
but one yearning for the hot splash himself
yet wanting it not too soon
sensing the other's pace and pitch
waiting for the involuntary gasp and groan
and hovering inevitability
and then the surge and spurt
and twin coming
seen double
somehow felt twice

After that we always forgot to turn out the light
until afterwards

—Another reason to share solo sex is for the pleasure of feeling another person's genitals and of having yours felt. I was in my late teens when I first scored with a woman who later became my wife, and the simple idea of touching any part of her body that I wished gave me an erection so firm that it was painful. And when I took her hand and put it around my cock, It was hotter than anything I had ever experienced.

I must agree with the letter writer whom I quoted earlier, however. There isn't any right or wrong here—it's all personal taste, but I have always preferred to have my cock held by a man. The strength of the grip, the sense of authority, taking charge, of owning me through my organ has always invited me to surrender to the moment, to relax and trust in him. .

But, regardless of the gender, we find pleasure in touching intimate body parts and having ours touched in return.

"I spent a lot of time once with this homosexual guy (I should point out that I am straight and married)," says Steven, a bartender in New Orleans whom I interviewed recently. "He never wanted anything from me, which is good, because he wouldn't have gotten it, except maybe I'd've kicked his ass. He'd come over to my place (this was when I was living alone), and we'd put on the television. I should tell you I never wore clothes in the apartment. So right from the beginning, that very first night, he asked me to just lay across his lap and he would play with me, no strings attached. He begged, so what was I going to do? I stretched out across his lap on the sofa and just ignored him, watched the idiot box, while he played with my cock.

"Well, after a while, I'm hard as a rock and breathing heavy. He's got me right on the brink, and even though he is going so slow and light I can hardly feel it, I know if he doesn't stop right then, I'm gonna shoot all over the place. And he does stop. It's like he was reading my mind. He just stopped until I calmed down, and started up again.

"For three hours he keeps me right on the edge, enough to drive nuts. And then he just keeps going, nice and slow, and it feels so good by the time I'm done twisting and moaning, I've got tears in my eyes."

This man told me repeatedly that he wasn't gay, and I believe him. I don't think the idea of playing with another man's penis is at all an attractive idea to him. But being masturbated by another man isn't gay sex as he sees it—it's an extension of his own solo sex activities.

—Erotic display—exhibitionism—is another motive for sharing solo sex with others. Mark, in Atlanta, writes: "When my first wife and I finally left that [fundamentalist] church, I began to accept myself as a masturbator, and it was with a great sense of relief that I told her about my solitary habit. And eventually I even showed her. After making love, we always left a great mess on the sheets, and so it was a surprise to her when I demonstrated by squirting into an empty glass that it really was only a few tablespoons or so of cum that came out! That was the first time anybody had seen me jerk off.

"Since that marriage broke up, I've made love with a couple of dozen different women, and most wound up watching me jerk off, too. Many women have never seen a guy cum himself. One woman (who always felt her breasts were too small) urged me to cum on her tits. Then she massaged the jism into them in hopes that it would make them grow.

"I've jerked off with a couple of guys, too. For awhile another man was part of our relationship; a favorite for me was to jerk off while the other guy screwed with my wife."

In the same vein, a man who signs himself The Wanker of Wilmette, writes, "My lover likes me to masturbate for her, and I enjoy indulging her, especially when she puts her mouth on me while I do it. Sometimes, she'll ask me to show her how I would play with myself if she weren't there.

"Sometimes we masturbate together. Sometimes we'll just tell each other about masturbation that day as a way into more conventional sex. She's even teased me into masturbating for her and a girlfriend's enjoyment. I confess I enjoyed that a lot.

"I like it that my lover and I openly talk about how we have always pleasured ourselves. We feel lucky to have found one another. Our relationship makes it easy for me to admit to and derive added pleasure from the lifelong relationship I have had with my own cock."

Solo sex is being more and more widely accepted since *Joy of Solo Sex* was published. It has come out of the closet. Many public figures are admitting that they enjoy it (as though we had our doubts!).

And of course attitudes are changing on college campuses. Not long ago, I received a letter from a young man who recently graduated from an Illinois university. He told me, "My college roommate and I used to jack off together almost every night—and occasionally during the day. He'd be in his bed and I in mine. We never touched each other, just looked and once in a while talked about favorite sensations and techniques. Mostly we just watched each other enjoying ourselves."

In fact, in some college situations, solo sex seems to be taken for granted as a natural aspect of life, and it isn't hidden. R.P., from New Orleans, gives the following account:

My college roommates and I jack off in front of each other all the time—well, mostly we do it at night after lights out or in the morning when we wake up, but we don't make any big secret out of it or go to any great lengths to hide what we're doing or try to be real quiet or anything. Mostly we just shove down the covers and go at it.

We can definitely hear each other, and if it's a moonlit night we can usually see each other, too. Actually, it's quite a turn-on sometimes to do it together—I almost always get a hard-on when somebody else starts in. (Well, actually I almost always get a hard-on when any sexual activity—real or imagined—is within a mile of my horny little mind.)

Sometimes one of us will get horny when reading a magazine or looking at pictures and start jacking off at other times of the day, too.

We just got all the shame and secrets right out in the open the first day of school—we all admitted that we like jacking off (a lot) and that we really hated having to restrict ourselves to occasions when nobody else was in the room (this is pretty rare anyway, since there are four of us in the same bedroom and we mostly have pretty much the same schedules). We were all used to having our own rooms at home and doing it all the time whenever we wanted to, and really didn't like the idea of going from two or three times a day to once or twice a week if we were lucky.

We also did away with that other roommate bugaboo—waking up in the morning with a big stiffy and being afraid to get out of bed for fear our room-mates would notice. We all get hard-ons all the time, don't we? So it's not like we never dreamed that we were the only guys with a stiff dick in bed in the morning. So we just hop right out of bed now with our flagpoles at attention if that happens to be the case when the alarm goes off. Most of us sleep naked anyway. Sometimes somebody makes some amusing comment, but usually nobody even notices.

If somebody walks into the room now and one of the other guys is jacking off, he just keeps on going, and the other guy will just usually make some comment like, "Ah ha! Caught you again, you horny bastard!"

The fact is, even the straightest guys are intrigued by other men's cocks and the heat of their lust. A Navy officer, heterosexual in both fact and fantasy all his life, told me that he had gone to a house of prostitution with a buddy in Yokasuka, Japan, during the Second World War. They picked up two girls who, back in their hotel room, "disrobed and got down on their knees at the end of the pallets and awaited our signal. I suggested to Pete the we begin our session by allowing the girls to sit astride our cocks.

"When we were on our backs, they understood and began stroking our rods until they were throbbing. I watched Pete's hot cock harden and he watched mine. The two girls sat astride us and slowly began moving. Then an odd thing happened. Pete and I reached out our arms and grasped each other's hand. The two girls laughed and joined hands also. We fucked away in our first position of the evening as a tightly-bound foursome. It was glorious fun watching the two gals ride our rods like small cowboys.

"The rest of the evening was spent exploring different positions. Each time, Pete and I would use identical positions as a way of communicating with one another.

"We fucked nearly two hours, resting in between orgasms. Several times I took Pete's gal and he took mine. I enjoyed the thought of my semen being mixed with Pete's inside his gal's small vagina. It was fantastic watching Pete fuck, moving his sweet ass up and down and tossing his head when he reached a climax."

Perhaps, in the strictest sense, this might be considered gay sex, although the men never touched each other's genitals. But from another perspective it's shared solo sex. The women, after all, are nothing more than masturbation devices in this context. The lust that the two men feel is contagious. They are sharing it back and forth, each rising higher on the sexual heat of the other. While they do not literally share the pleasure of feeling each other and being felt by the other, there's every indication that they are doing precisely that through the surrogate bodies of the women. And the description of the activities, each man enjoying the pleasure both of erotic display and voyeurism, is clear.

Sharing solo sex isn't something we must learn to do. It's as natural as breathing—it's what we do as kids. Those who have forced themselves to "outgrow" it deny themselves one of life's greatest—and safest—pleasures.

Chapter Seven

Erotic Display

Being nude is the natural state of humankind, and, frankly, it has taken some very warped and sexually perverted thinking to find anything indecent or obscene about the naked body. Just as the air and the sea and forest are natural, so the unclothed human body is natural.

Nakedness in the out-of-doors is an aesthetic, inspiring and fulfilling experience. Anyone who hasn't tried it is missing out on an enormously valuable venture. And one reason that being nude, even in a pristine and solitary way, is satisfying is that it has the halo of Eros surrounding it. We are lifted up above our ordinary, mundane lives when we are nude. Especially outdoors.

But this chapter is not about simple nudity outdoors. It's about nakedness with a purpose—solo and consensual exhibitionism, more generally called erotic display.

In his classic and controversial study, *The Ethics of Sexual Acts*, Rene Guyon wrote: "What is today called exhibitionism was once a normal act, freely permitted and frequently resorted to in societies where the sexual sense was not regarded as shameful. Diogenes, who masturbated 'publicly in the street, in the middle of a crowd, that others may follow his example,' might find his action discussed from the philosophical point of view, but he was not prosecuted for having committed an outrage on public decency. Today, in our anti-sexual societies, this act seems fundamentally abnormal, because it is in contradiction with—we might even say in rebellion against—all the accepted conventions of permissible behavior. In this sense exibitionism is only to be found in anti-sexual civilizations: because in other societies there is no ground for regarding as abnormal or reprehensible an act which in no way outrages the accepted conventions—just as the crime of theft could not, strictly speaking, exist in a completely communist society. In numerous races of the ancient world, the role of the sexual organs and the sexual act was so frequently recognized that no one dreampt of condemning behavior which was regarded as a normal expression of this desire and its satisfaction."

Guyon concludes that exhibitionism, whether or not leading to copulation, is natural and "thus essentially in harmony with human nature, however much [exhibitionistic acts] may offend against convention and taboo."

Exhibitionism In Nature

Of course, bringing attention to one's self as a sex object is common in other species. The pheasant calls to hens in the vicinity with an ear-splitting screech. When she approaches, he runs in front of her, prances back and forth, and fans out his brilliantly colored tail. As Hy Freeman explains in *Sex Link*, "These maneuverings—she turning away and he running in front of her and displaying—may go on for some time, but eventually she'll succumb to the splendors of his gorgeous raiment and consent to copulation." Similar erotic display takes place among many species of birds.

Although the male fiddler crab may be a drab brownish-gray much of the time, when he's in the mood for sex his body rapidly changes into an array of dazzling colors. Apparently the penises on fiddler crabs aren't much to rave about, or even notice, so nature has provided one huge claw which, in a frenzied dance of erotic display, the fiddler lifts heavenward and waves frantically. His colors grow even brighter as the female approaches and submits to his potency.

A West African baboon known as the mandrill has no need of feathers or claws in erotic display—instead, he flashes a crimson-colored penis flanked by two blue scrotal patches. Whether in love or war, he's quick to flash a fully erect penis to make his point. And apparently he believes in doubling his pleasure and his fun—his face is a carbon copy of his genitals, with bright red nose and naked blue cheeks. His buttocks are also bright crimson.

Sex Outdoors

My guess is that virtually every man with a normal amount of testosterone flowing through his veins has known the desire for erotic display. And a courageous minority have acted on that urge—although for the most part without an audience. As one man, now in his mid-thirties, wrote:

"I guess I pulled off some pretty crazy stunts. Like hiking naked in the woods, my shorts in my hand. One time I climbed a pine tree, naked, except for shoes. (I started out barefoot, but it was too painful.) I got pretty damn close to the top, straddled a branch and leaned back against the trunk. It seemed like I could see to the end of the earth, and I just had to have an orgasm. Like that cereal peddler on television says, it was the right thing to do."

This gentleman had a girlfriend—now his wife—who enjoyed sharing in his erotic display. "One time we were staying in Baltimore in a hotel a few streets west of The Block," he says. "It was right across from a fire house. One night, about two-thirty in the morning, we went out on the wrought-iron balcony—it was about the sixth floor. She stretched out on the concrete. I climbed on top. We were both naked, cars passing below, the dark windows of the buildings all around. Then the alarm goes off and the fire engines start pulling out. We were looking down at them, my bare ass pounding up and down and with the both of us moaning and groaning. It was great."

The two of them joined a nudist club, primarily a puritanical family resort. "I don't know what got into Carol that one afternoon," he says. "She never did anything quite like that before. We were in the pool, and it was crowded—kids, old folks, everybody right up close to each other and splashing, yelling. Suddenly, I felt her hand on my dick. I looked down, but the water was splashing and churning, and you couldn't see anything. Slowly she kept pulling on my cock. I kept looking around, first out of fear that somebody'd spot us and we'd get our asses kicked out of the camp. But then, when I started getting the feeling and breathing hard and getting hot, the idea that someone would spot us became a real turn-on. The water was up to our shoulders, so I started thrusting to her hand, really moving my hips. People were swimming by, brushing against us.

"I could feel the heat in my face but no one seemed to notice. I threw my head back, closed my eyes, felt others bumping against me, and shot about six gobs into her hand. Whew! Unforgettable."

I don't care how young or old you are, sex is never better then when it's enjoyed out-of-doors. Not all outdoor sex is great, mind you. My first experience balling in nature happened on a warm summer afternoon in the Poconos of Pennsylvania. My comrade, Nancy, who eventually became my first wife, walked beside me hand-in-hand through a pine grove. Finally, we settled down on a soft bed of needles and went at it with predictable clumsiness.

Suddenly a swarm of ravenous deer flies descended upon us. If you know anything about deer flies, you know that they are not intimidated by having their bodies crushed by human hands. Whatever remains of them continues to bite. Like a few people I know, they are more interested in gluttony than survival. That part of my mind which had not become oblivious to reality pondered whether I would succeed in ejaculating before dying of blood loss.

I survived—although, the next day, I found welts—torturously itching welts—on my buttocks, thighs, even my scrotum. And Nancy? She faired even worse, having placed her butt on a patch of pine needle-covered poison ivy.

Thankfully, that doesn't comprise the spirit of outdoor sex, much less the ecstasy of it. At its best, the ideal is more like this:

I do want to pass along one of my first (and favorite) jack-off experiences that occurred when I was 13 years old. Ever since childhood I have been fascinated by male genitals. When I was about 12, I experienced by my first dry orgasm as I soaped up my pint-sized boner in the shower and played with it until my knees buckled with the first sensation of orgasm. I was hooked and eagerly demonstrated my new-found joy to my buddies.

One warm summer day when I was 13, my buddy Dave and I took a walk deep into the woods. Dave was my age and was barefoot and bare chested, wearing only a pair of shorts. I became excited as I admired his chest and smooth stomach. Soon our conversation turned to sex and we decided to show each other our dicks and dropped our pants. Although we were the same age, Dave's cock wasn't quite as developed as mine, but I didn't care. Dave was fascinated by the size and firmness of my dick and soon we

117

were fondling each other's genitals. Dave shuddered, grabbed his dick and milked a clear drop of pre-cum from the tip of it, and asked if I could "make jizz?" I knew what he meant and told him I never had. Dave grabbed the base of my cock with one hand and started rubbing the palm of his other hand over and around the swollen head of my cock (a technique I have never been able to duplicate as skillfully as my friend). Boy, did he ever know what he was doing— he played me like a violin! I whimpered and moaned as my cock throbbed and lurched while he teased me to the brink of orgasm. I couldn't hold back any longer—I looked down and watched in amazement as I blasted my first load of cream into the palm of my buddy's hand.

Dave was almost as dazed as I was. He wiped the last drop of cum from the tip of my cock and wiped it on a fallen tree trunk. That tree trunk became my own personal shrine of manhood. Eager to repay the favor, I rubbed and fondled Dave's hanging balls as he lay down in the grass and jacked himself off while I watched.

Later, I asked Dave how he learned his technique—it seems his older teenaged brother had no inhibitions about dropping his pants and beating off in front of Dave as he watched TV, studied, etc. Sure wish I had an older brother!

Everyone should display his penis proudly, according to Leonardo da Vinci:

"It seems, therefore, that this creature [the penis] has often a life and intelligence separate from the man, and it would appear that the man is in the wrong by being ashamed of giving it a name or to exhibit it, seeking rather to cover and conceal what he ought to adorn and display with ceremony as a ministrant"

So widespread is the hunger for the phallus to be nakedly displayed in nature that it might be considered a universal, natural instinct. "I enjoy the freedom of nudity," writes R.P. of Hanover, MA, "and have taken surreptitious opportunities to go naked in the woods, even practicing frottage on unsuspecting tree trunks. I also swim bareass at night. There is a sense of uninhibited liberty and, sometimes, unbridled promiscuity that is total ecstasy and exhilaration. I think that is probably one of the reasons why nudist colonies, even if I did have the opportunity to join, wouldn't appeal to me—their repeated disclaimer against sexuality. I think being able to bound around with an erection is half the enjoyment."

One prolific correspondent, H.R. of Vermont, keeps a journal of his erotic rituals. One morning, too sexually distracted to work, he took a walk in the woods behind his house:

> Maybe my cock will go down by the time I get back. It's very, very sensitive at this point. Rubbing the head of my dick with my left hand—rubbing the fingers back and forth across the head. Try breathing in cadence with my walking. Every once in a while a passing tree reaching out caresses my balls.
>
> I've been walking for a few minutes now.... stroking it with one hand, sometimes two hands. I feel all charged up now....cock is silky smooth. I'm touching it really gently, bottom to top, bumping balls at the bottom. Left hand on my nipple. My balls slap against my thighs as I walk—they feel really big and full of come. Breathing faster now, stroking faster now, rubbing my balls with the tips of my fingers. Precome leaks out. Cock stands up hard. Pulling down on my balls and up on my dick—squeeze both really tight. More fast stroking...

Clothes Make the Man

Just as women have always been able to display their breasts without breaking the law, men, too, now take advantage of fashion to exhibit their genitalia. One of the more popular garments is the spandex tights. They clutch the buttocks cheeks and even the crevice as though they were skin, and if the wearer so desires, they can cling to the uplifted genitalia so tightly that both testes and penis are there to behold.

Soft cotton or nylon lounging pants, similar to pajamas and without a fly, can also be a great turn-on. Here's an account from H.R.'s journal:

I put on five "ponytailer" cock rings today—they're soft elastic fabric bands designed to hold pony tails, but just the right size for cock and balls. My cock makes a big lump in my pants—gets bigger as I talk about it. [H.R. dictates his rituals while performing them and transcribes them later.] I like showing basket. I don't naturally have a lot of basket. My dick kind of hangs down straight and soft, kind of disappears in the folds of my pants. Putting a couple of ponytailers around it makes a big difference. Pulls my balls forward—cock comes forward, it all sort of juts out. Rubs against my pants in a totally different way. My balls are real sensitive—they sort of scrape the seam on my crotch. Then my dick hardens up. Lengthens down. Skin peels back off the head. Head rubs up against the pants, getting stimulation. Doing that and talking about it makes my dick real hard. I hope I don't see anyone I know. It's pretty obscene sticking down six or seven inches, pushing out against the pants leg.

I have fantasies of people noticing, stopping me, taking me home, having a quickie on the way to work. It's real nice to have your dick real hard—mine's been hard almost the entire last day. Thing about walking down the street is that you can't touch yourself at all. There are people around. You have to concentrate on the feeling that your clothing makes. I'm wearing hospital greens as long johns. They're nice and smooth and silky.

Discretion, of course, is the better part of valor, and as H.R. nears the busy square of the small town where he lives, he decides to turn around and go back home. He's had all the thrill of erotic display without breaking the law.

Many men have modified ordinary garments for sexual pleasure. The most common alteration by far is cutting out the bottom of one or both pockets.

"I have an old sweatshirt that hangs down to my crotch," says a Philadelphia man. "The whole thing's baggy—you really can't tell where anything begins and ends. So I jam my hands in my pockets, grab my balls in one, my dick head in the other, and walk along at a good clip right down on west Market Street, thousands of people all around me. It's left-right, left-right, pull balls-pull dick, pull balls-pull dick. When I feel myself getting ready to come, I try to get into an alley or quiet side street—it feels so good jerking off in front of all those people I'm just afraid one of these days I might whip it out and let them all see it. Actually, I don't think I'd get that carried away, but who knows? The bigger concern is that everyone would see my face turning beet red, see my mouth drop open, my eyes close—they'd figure out what the hell I was doing and yell for the cops."

A variation on the theme is the rope-tied jogging pants minus the front. Wearing this in public obviously requires a knee length raincoat or overcoat. Once again, the pockets can be removed.

Or, you can go really creative: tie a long cord snugly behind the glans of your penis, then behind the back of your neck and down the sleeve of the raincoat. Bend your elbows slightly, and tie the end of the string around your middle finger. Now, every time you straighten your elbow, you'll be tugging on your dick. If it's already pointing up when you fasten the string, you'll have plenty of leverage to give it a resounding yank whenever you wish. Although it isn't likely to lead to orgasm, you can certainly entertain yourself.

A variation: remove the zipper from an old pair of dress slacks and replace it with two pieces of Velcro. (The trousers ought to be baggy at the crotch and fit snugly at the waist.) Snip off the belt loops at either side of the buckle.

Now, the instant you are alone—and be *sure* you're alone—you may let your little friend out for a breath of fresh of air, and seclude him again within two seconds. Or, you can wear the raincoat and take him for a nice, long walk.

Let's Go to the Movies

Most of you remember the Pee Wee Herman fiasco—the entertainer went to an adult film theater and did what I would conservatively estimate one in ten men at such theaters do—he gave himself an orgasm. Or at least he was attempting to do that when, ignoring the right of consenting adults to assemble for that purpose in that place, he was *arrested*. In that instant, his career—at least as a children's entertainer—was destroyed. An entire cross section of society condemned him as a pervert. (I have no doubt that some of them went on to masturbate to the fantasy that they were watching Pee Wee in action.)

Do you see how socially sick arrests like these are? In adult theaters—and in brothels—we have found a way to give safe and sane expression to normal compulsions. But, because abnormal people consider them evil, we are making criminals of those who simply want sexual release in the presence of consenting adults. The Pee Wee movie house offered men the opportunity to be exhibitionists and voyeurs for the price of a ticket. They chose not to go out and to approach innocent women and children, causing them emotional trauma and potential psychological damage. They played the game as the participants understand it to be played—and for that Pee Wee was prosecuted.

Should you engage in such theatrics, keep in mind that, technically, it is illegal. Of course, millions of men have done it, and in most major cities and countless smaller ones the powers-that-be usually look the other way, perhaps realizing that these movie houses serve a significant benefit. The exception, of course, is during the months immediately preceding an election. Sex-bashing gets votes.

On the Road Again

Nothing breaks the monotony of a long drive quite as pleasantly as stripping nude and fondling your genitals hour after hour—or so I've been told. B.B. of Allentown, Pennsylvania, writes, "I had to take about a two-hundred mile trip on Sunday and, do you know, I jerked off most of the time while driving! I can keep from cumming by slowing down my rhythm and then even just holding my cock in my hand for a while as I drive. When I'm ready, I just shoot it into a tissue. I always keep a box handy on the floor.

"The best blast if you're an exhibitionist is the eighteen-wheelers. They can look right down on you and see exactly what you are doing, and most of them have been around the block enough not to get pissed off when they see what's going on. One summer afternoon I stripped naked going north on ninety-five through Virginia and deliberately drove past every big rig I could find while poking my hard pecker in the air. One guy saw my CB antenna on my roof and said, 'I really like the eggs in your basket.' To tell you the truth, I got embarrassed, but damned it if some other guy didn't answer, 'Well, thank you, sir!'

"You can always tell which truckers are interested. They speed up to keep with you as you creep past them. They keep their window even with yours when you slow down, and if they slow down, too, that's all it takes to get me off.

"I don't want to get it on with them. I just want them to watch while I cream. Once, when I shot, the trucker blasted his horn. Another time, the guy waved his jockey shorts out the window. He was beating off along with me."

It's always wise to keep your shorts around your ankles. For one thing, you might be stopped in a random check (or because you are having so much fun that you are nonchalantly moving at fifty miles above the speed limit). Another major screw-up is to pass—or be passed by—a bus. Chances are good that at least a few of the passengers who will be treated with a glimpse of your raging erection are fundamentalists who have never seen such sin and will fret until you're behind bars.

Consensual Public Display

Believe it or not, there are people who get paid for public exhibitionism, from nude dancing to performing live on stage, and, of course, making sexually explicit videos and films. The problem with that kind of work is that it's—work.

As a hobby, being a sex star can be strictly pleasurable. K.L. of New Orleans writes, "My favorite way is to jerk off in public places for others to watch or join in. Public solo sex is sometimes dangerous, so I wouldn't advise a novice to try it alone. Get an experienced buddy and go at it and take notes.

"The best time of the year to do things publicly is during the summer. I can wear skimpy shorts and that makes for easy exposure and quick concealing if necessary.

"Usually, I start out doing something expected of me in a public place, like playing pool or shooting pinball. Then, given an audience, I will coyly at first start to pull on my dick until it gets too hard to conceal easily. Then, at the pool table or the pinball machine, I get more into it, stroking my need for enjoyment and excitement. I have had great success in the past and will probably continue to get further success stories under my belt.

"Once, while doing a little show by a pinball machine, I was 'caught' by the bartender. He proceeded to 'reprimand' me but closed the doors and 'punished' me by making me get on the bar and do it for 'the whole class' to see. Well, what can I say? It was great!"

If erotic display is important to you, think creatively about ways to meet your own needs without offending others. And I want to stress those last few words, for I feel that some exhibitionists destroy the hope of bringing others to know freedom in bodyspirit. I have no patience, for example, with people who have sex in public on a nude beach when they ought to realize that they may well be 1) embarrassing a young man or woman into fleeing forever any further exploration of nudism; 2) triggering the closure of that beach to nudism (as happened, at Jacob Riis Park in New York when gays persisted in having sex in front of elderly residents). Having pleasure at the expense of others is not just selfish and immature—it's detrimental to the unity of our extended selves.

Having said that, I have equally little patience with those closed-minded individuals who deny the natural instinct of erotic display and try to stifle its expression under pressure of law. What is true of us, what is real, is not changed just because it is made illegal. You can beat a rock into pebbles, and into dust, but, when you are done beating it, the dust is still rock.

125

PART TWO

Deep Sex and Bodyspirit

Chapter Eight

Make the Next Time
Your First Time Again

I've heard it said, "As the years go by, sex just keeps getting better." And from one perspective that's unquestionably true. Youngsters enjoy sex the way they do food—they gulp down great chunks of hamburger. They swallow French fries whole, wash them down with anything wet, enjoy the titillating taste of salt-flavored grease, and declare it all a great meal. For most adolescents, truly fine cuisine would be a waste of money. *All* their appetites are both voracious and coarse.

As we grow older, we appreciate subtlety, innuendo, technique. We learn that any sort of sex is wonderful beyond words, but that sex with fantasy is better. So is experimental sex, gymnastic sex, exotic, bizarre, uninhibited, kinky, gross, risky, creative—in fact, *any sex that is fresh and refreshing, different, new,* is even more fun than the same old same old.

That's why first-time orgasms are mind-blowingly special. A twelve-year-old boy says, "That was like nothing else in my whole *life!*"

Says a man in his late teens, "I'd had some wet dreams— you know, I'd be half asleep and half awake, and this real good feeling would go all through me and I'd wake up with some gook in my underpants. But it wouldn't be real intense and, by the way, I didn't worry about it, although nobody ever told me this was going to happen to me. It just seemed okay, and I guess I thought it must have something to do with sex, although I didn't know what.

"Well, I live in north Philadelphia, and one day when I was like twelve I went past this alley in this bombed-out neighborhood, and there's these two guys—must've been seventeen, eighteen—bare chested, their pants around their ankles so they were just standing there naked, sliding their hands back and forth over what seemed to me, being a kid, dicks big enough to be on horses. I guess they were just standing there waiting for somebody to pass, some kid or woman or something, so they could get their kicks showing off their hard dicks.

"Well, I was like hypnotized, and I stood there staring at them, and in about ten seconds that must of turned them on because they both shot three or four feet at the same time. Scared the hell out of me, and I ran all the way back home.

"That night in bed, I started rubbing my dick the same as I saw them doing, and it wasn't long before I had this feeling that just seemed to open me up. I can't describe it, I really can't. All I can say is, I've never been the same since then, and that was like six years ago."

I think this man is wise not to try to describe it, the feeling of orgasm. Anyone capable of describing orgasms isn't having very good ones. It is an *otherworldly* experience, beyond the reach of human language. I truly believe that there is something metaphysical in the orgasm, beyond the mundane reality of our everyday lives. I will have a great deal more to say about that later. Now, let me return to the subject at hand, so to speak.

Here's how J.M. of Delaware describes his uniquely feverish early sexual experiences:

> My earliest recollection is at age ten when male classmates were showing each other "dirty" postcard photos, and using four-letter words and talking about

jerking off. Coming from a very puritanically minded family, all this was completely new to me—learning that my penis was a cock, and a lady's organ was a cunt, and my rear end was an ass. My parents *never* once discussed anything about sex with me—and all I learned was from the boys and from experimentation. I was scared to death when I first jerked off into my Boy Scout kerchief, but evidently I liked it because that kerchief became so starchy stiff from continual use, I could no longer stuff it easily behind my bookcase, and certainly couldn't wear it again. I secretly (in the dead of night) disposed of it in the garbage and then started all over again on an old pair of underwear etc....

I could hardly wait to get home from school, way back then, to go up to my room, or into the bathroom to get it off quickly—and whenever my mother went to the store, that was the signal for me to run naked and free all through the house, having a private orgy with my little stiff cock. I'd keep watching from the window, and when I saw her returning I'd dress and start my homework.

I soon discovered that there were writings on public toilet walls, and these were a fantastic source of pleasure for me. Everywhere I went, I would seek out the men's room and always go in the stall to urinate so I could read the scrawls and jack off in the process. And soon I was getting a kick out of adding my own lewd ideas and drawing my own very crude pictures of cocks and balls, and I thrilled to the idea of others reading what I wrote and jerking themselves off, too. And of course in time I discovered little glory holes in the walls, and I saw others' hands busy at work pulling their cocks, too. And then, when a hand reached under the stall, that was another breakthrough—and so my sex life grew.

What's your strongest erotic memory from those years? Maybe it wasn't your very first time, but early on. And perhaps you weren't alone. Robert, of Irvington, New Jersey, writes, "I was thirteen when I got my first job working part-time for Hymie and Gerta Potofsky in their little neighborhood grocery store. You don't have them anymore—everything's supermarkets these days. Anyway, I was a blond-haired, blue-eyed, skinny, innocent kid, and, although I didn't know it at the time, Hymie had the hots for me."

Young Bobby was so naive that he had no idea what was going on when Hymie reached under his apron, squeezed the boy's genitals, and slipped two quarters into his hand. He did the routine several more times that Saturday morning (Bobby worked 9:00 am to 1:00 PM, Saturdays only), and finally the youth understood.

"I didn't like it," he says today. "It was wrong for a man to be touching me like that. But it was like fifteen dollars more than I would have made working those four hours, so I figured I could live with it."

Ultimately, the relationship lasted until Bobby was seventeen years old and began dating girls. He always set the parameters—no anal activities, he would receive but not give oral sex, no kissing, and he would masturbate the man for twenty dollars. He never did feel completely comfortable with the relationship. Yet, as he says, he had the most memorable orgasm of his life a few weeks after beginning work at the delicatessen.

"I finished that Saturday at one as usual," he says. "Mrs. Potofsky had gone shopping for the afternoon, and the store was empty. Hymie took me into the back room. I was scared. I didn't know what to expect.

"He stood me in front of a full length mirror on a closet door. I felt him fooling around with my belt and zipper, and then my pants fell to my feet. He couldn't see my body because the apron—it was one of those you hang around your neck— still covered me. I could feel him pulling my underpants down, and saw them around my feet. I was nervous—I really was. And yet I was breathing hard with excitement.

"He reached underneath the apron and pulled my T-shirt up to my arm-pits. Then, I felt his hand on my cock. It was already hard, and I guess I knew I wanted to feel him take hold of it, and yet I didn't want to be responsible.

"He lifted the apron up and threw it over my shoulder, and there I was staring at my reflection, my hard dick firm in this man's hand, my cock head jumping out every time he smoothed the foreskin back. I felt his lips on my neck. He whispered, 'Look how beautiful you are, how big that cock of yours is.'"

Bobby began moaning involuntarily. His body began trembling, his knees buckled. Hymie reached around his tiny waist and supported him. He leaned back against the man, thrusting his pelvis forward, shoving his dick into Hymie's hand.

"Until then, I never imagined how beautiful I was," he says. "Beautiful, sexy. I was Hymie's sex object—and I'd never love any feeling more."

In a moment it happened. Thrashing his head from side to side, staring at his ejaculating reflection in the mirror, he reached over his shoulder to clutch Hymie's head and pull the man's cheek against his throat.

"I had tears running down my face," he says today. "That's how good it felt."

Understand what happens to the newly pubescent boy— what happened to Bobby, and to you; what happened to me: We were in seventh grade, or thereabouts. Two years earlier, perhaps, we strolled around the school yard alone on our lunch hour and thought that, although we certainly lacked a great many cold, hard facts about the world, we understood its values and motivations. We understood greed, jealousy, the drive to fame and power. We understood the teachers and their beliefs and our parents, and the reasons they all behaved as they did. In fact, we concluded with great self-satisfaction, we understood all we needed ever to know about human motives and behavior.

Then, at age twelve, we learned about sex, and we were humbled by the depth of our previous ignorance. But even that was book knowledge, not practical experience. Of course there was the unexplainable tingling in our lower abdomens and a hardening of our penises at the most inopportune times. For example, I remember taking the Number 25 Springfield Avenue bus to Grandma's house in Newark, New Jersey, on several occasions. That street was made of cobblestones then—still might be for all I know. The rhythmic bouncing of the seat created the Boing Effect. Now, my twelve-year-old erect penis was probably an inch and a half long. Yet, I was mortified that anyone would notice my shameful display, so I stayed in my seat for three stops beyond the one that I had wanted, until my erection subsided.

But that wasn't sex with a capital "O." It was still everyday, ordinary life.

Then there came the night when I was looking through the encyclopedia on a school assignment concerning "segregation," and found myself leafing through the pages to find "sex," and from there I was redirected to "reproduction," about which I could understand not a word. At that point, my father, semi-intoxicated, stumbled through the door and inquired into what I was reading.

"The encyclopedia," I told him.

"I can see that, goddammit. What are you reading *about*?"

"Sex," I mumbled.

"You want to know about sex? I'll tell you anything you want to know. Just wait here."

He spent the next hour at a bar getting drunker, returned, and, in slurred but much more understandable words than the encyclopedia had offered, gave me the full details as he understood them. Here was a tough man of the streets who prided himself in being honest, even brutal, with the truth.

"That feeling is everything in the world," he said. "A man will kill for it. Die for it. He just shoves his dick in a woman, pounds away, and it comes—that feeling!"

So, I asked the logical question: "How else can I get that feeling? Is there a way?"

Miraculously, he was silent for a moment. Finally he said, "Yeah, there's a way, but I ain't gonna tell you. You'll go crazy and get cancer and all kinds of shit." So he never told me. I assume he imagined that, at age twelve, I would go out forthwith and find macho fulfillment by impregnating chicks, since he neglected to tell me how to avoid fertilizing them. But I found out about jerking off, and within hours I lay on my grandparents' bed, while they entertained my father and mother in the adjoining room, separated only by a flimsy curtain. It was not the ideal environment for my first solo sex experience, but by then lust had built to an overpowering level. I unzipped my pants, fished my penis through the opening in my jockey shorts, and began massaging the foreskin back and forth over my tiny glans.

It took only a moment—I don't know how I kept from crying out. I don't want to be melodramatic, but that moment was something I don't know how to describe. It is like seeing the face of God. (In fact, I will argue later that it is indeed seeing the face of God.) In those few seconds, the only self I had ever known ceased to exist. Yes, "I" ceased to be, and where "I" had been was bright light and joy in that *feeling*.

I don't know why I never felt terror. It was as overwhelming as general anesthesia, as utterly annihilating of the self as death, more disorienting than any amusement park tilt-a-whirl. Yet, I felt no fear, but ran deeper and deeper into the bright light of orgasm. And, although I could not have come close to articulating it then, I remember feeling, "Yes, this is *life* at last. This is what I want always, always."

I'm convinced that the intensity of that feeling never changes. Both the letters in my files from scores of men in their seventies and eighties and the formal research published in medical journals show that the measurable intensity of orgasm doesn't change very significantly over the years. But for many men, something certainly *does* change: Our appetite for orgasm lags. Lust dissipates. We can take sex or leave it—and often we choose to leave it.

I'm not talking about impotence, although lack of sexual desire might lead to it. I'm talking about the typical regression from pubescence to mature adulthood in the way we respond to the idea of sex.

Three factors are behind the Take-It-Or-Leave-It syndrome. Now, I'm talking in generalities. For example, you could have a physical condition that turns down your sex drive. It might be something as simple as taking decongestants for a cold or sinus problem. But, assuming that you're in good health and not using medications or recreational drugs excessively, I'm going to show you how to restore the joy of youth to your sexuality, whether it's solo or with another—or others.

Becoming a Boy Again

As we grow from adolescence to mature adulthood, the intensity of orgasm remains virtually the same, but for most men some sort of change definitely does take place. No longer are we shattered into nonexistence by the ecstasy radiating through the void of our bodies and our universe. The explanation is simple and normal enough: In our youth, our orgasms exploded through a *vacuum of inexperience*. In the years from age twelve through—let's say forty—we've had any number of sexual experiences and orgasms. (Those who averaged three orgasms a week during those years have had 4,368 of them. And men with higher sex drives may have had at least two orgasms a day—or 20,384. In case you're counting, at one ounce per ejaculation, that's more than 635 gallons of semen—enough to fill thirteen bath tubs.)

That experience is a mountain of pleasure that few of us would exchange for anything—but it's still a mountain, and it separates us from the naive innocence that made our youthful sexuality incomparable. Add to that the clutter and distractions of everyday life that bog us down decade after decade and you see that it isn't the miracle of the orgasm but our relationship to it that has changed.

But you can regain that youthful enthusiasm you had for sex, and I'm going to show you how right now. Remember that anonymous poem:

Across the fields of Yesterday
There sometimes comes to me
A little child all lost in play—
The child I used to be.

Make no mistake—that child is still there. Deep beneath the neocortical crevices of your outer brain, nestled in the recesses of your passion-generating limbic system, the child you were—his personality, enthusiasm, and desires—will always exist at the heart of the man you are. You can find him in all his freshness and wonder—if that's really what you want to do.

The key to ecstasy, it seems to me—whether it's erotic, spiritual, creative, athletic, or what have you—is in the loss of self. If there is a single great curse on the human species it is self-awareness, self-consciousness. When the priest in the book *The Thornbirds* spoke of the birds who live among bushes with giant thorns, he told his lover that sometimes, by accident, they pierce their own breasts, when all they really needed to do was to avoid the thorn bushes in the first place. And then he said, "And we humans do the same—except we *know*. We *know*!"

That self-consciousness leads to irrational guilt, shame, a sense that, because we are not perfect, we need to be punished for something—usually sex. Many thoughtful writers and philosophers, along with scientists of the personality, have condemned this aspect of our self-awareness as damaging, making some people emotional cripples. Arthur Koestler, in *The Ghost in the Machine,* suggests that the explosive growth of the human neocortex is a cancer that may well destroy humanity.

Although I don't want to belabor this point, it's crucial that you understand this if you're to take a step back into what is indeed the innocence of youth. The worst problem with our intellects isn't their capacity to rationalize, to problem solve, to retain information—not even to scheme and plot. The problem is that they make us too self-centered, self-absorbed, *self-aware*.

Although I have known many writers and many artists, the majority of whom frankly had very large egos, I believe that no writer or other artist ever created his work while being aware of his own existence. Before and after, sure. But while the work was in progress, he was *absorbed*.

Athletes whose sports require instant reactions—downhill skiers, boxers, football players—know too well that once they are distracted by self-related thinking, they're on their way to failure.

Years ago, when I faced an audience to present one of my first lectures on sex and aging at Grossingers in the Catskills, I suddenly thought, this is me in front of all these people. I absolutely froze. It took me several seconds to get back on course and concentrate on the material rather than myself.

Being self-centered has its place, of course. We enjoy studying our nude bodies in mirrors, dressing well, being clever among our friends at parties. But I'm more convinced than ever that there is a certain quality of person who, since the beginning of history, has sought to escape the confines of the narrower self, dissolve into his greater, unconscious being and leave his thinking brain behind.

That's precisely what narcotics do, of course—they erase the walls of our day-to-day personalities. So does alcohol, and charismatic religion. So does orgasm, the *petit mort,* the little death, so named by the French, aptly describing the effective nonexistence of one in the throes of ecstasy.

Escape Your Conscious Self

Yes, I know: "The unexamined life is not worth living." "Know thyself." And so forth. But listen: A child can observe his toes and watch them move and giggle, and learn all sorts of things about how his muscles make those cute little digits work—and never for a moment be aware that he is watching and learning.

A teenager can study his erect penis, feel the throb start deep in his prostate, involuntarily spasm into the whole shaft, study with eyes wide the pre-ejaculatory fluid—and never be conscious of his own presence in what is transpiring. That's what I mean by losing the self. It's synonymous with the innocence of the Garden of Eden and of childhood.

Those of you who read *The Joy of Solo Sex* may recall the process whereby we tried to escape self-consciousness. It included 1) Sweeping the Stage; 2) Creating the Image; 3) Concentrating on the Sensory Experiences of the Fantasy. We were allowing ourselves to be absorbed, as an artist does, by the work of art, the fantasy.

That's why sexually explicit *materials* can be wonderful. They help one to escape self-consciousness—not easy in this hectic world—and concentrate on the healing power of sacred lust and orgasm. In fact, one celebrator of the body has written to me, "A sacred relic or icon is something that facilitates a deeper religious experience for the worshipper. If the body and its sexuality are sacred, as you say, then for some people pornography, which facilitates orgasm, can actually be sacred. So why do they try to make us feel ashamed? We should all stand up and shout, 'I read pornography and I love it!'"

Sexually explicit photography and literature, as I prefer to call it (pornography has been given a bad name, like masturbation) may have its place in helping you to return to the intensity of youthful sexuality. There are many other triggers, as well, including your own imagination. But triggers are the second

139

step, and the first is much more important. It's the starting point of being unself-conscious.

Is it possible for you to do that? Many, many people simply can't escape themselves. A dairy blows up in Texas and their immediate response is, "I'll be paying more for milk with all those cows dead—but less for beef."

Can you find contentment in *simply observing*? Can you find contentment in watching ants carry their baggage across the pavement, in following that line of cargo carriers for half a block or more, first in one direction to find the source of their prosperity, then in the other to learn its destination. There is nothing demonstrably profitable in all this. It is curiosity-driven. You drink it all in without having to think a single conscious thought.

Recently a close friend and colleague—I'll call him A.E.—built a house across from a lovely park. A large deck looks out over a lake with small islands, ducks, turtles, even a few swans. A.E. is a business executive, constantly on the go, and so I was surprised when he confided, "Harold, sometimes hours pass and I do nothing but look out on that park. I don't think I have a single thought in all that time." Afterward he's refreshed—and often horny!

Can you simply *do without thinking*? Too impatient to simply observe, Robert Bahr, when he lived in the woods of Pennsylvania, found the path to regaining his childhood through mindless physical activity. With a wedge and a sledge hammer, nude, but in ninety-degree July heat, he'd split a cord of logs or, using a sharp scythe, he'd cut a hiking path through wild grape vines and briars. He'd build stone walls. It was this unthinking physical activity that brought him out of his neocortical self and in contact with his inner child.

Others do it jogging, swimming, hiking—anything that allows an emptying of the conscious mind. That was the purpose of the exercise in *Joy* in which we concentrated on a *Perfect Peace Scene*. In observing that scene, in relaxing into it, we were able to put aside self-consciousness.

How long must you escape your conscious self? That's impossible to answer, of course, because it depends on who you are, how thoroughly you escape, and your sex drive, among other things. The goal is to become *asexual*, and that isn't easy for everyone. The reason sex had so overwhelming an impact on the youth you were is that you did not anticipate it. You could not have imagined it, at least experientially. It caught you off guard.

That's what we're striving for, that complete absence of self-consciousness and sex-consciousness. Be *sure* not to allow yourself any even momentary thoughts regarding sex. Here are some things that will try to pop into your head:

—I wonder if I've been unself-conscious long enough?

—I think my dick's getting hard.

—I wonder if this is going to work.

—I want to have an orgasm, dammit.

The Turning Point

Depending upon your typical frequency of sex activity, the turning point can come within hours—or weeks. You may well end up on the longest sex fast of your life, but you'll also notice a heightened alertness, an increased edge to your senses. Your body will seem to be fine-tuning itself. Your genitals will feel as though they are slowly enlarging, swelling (of course you must ignore the feeling and refuse to think about it).

When you've reached the stage where naively and unself-consciously, sexual hunger overwhelms your day-to-day life, it's time for the trigger. One of the best approaches, because it is actually the experience you are trying to recapture, is to recall those early erotic experiences. K.J. of Los Angeles lusts to these memories:

> I was about 13 years old when I first discovered the **joys** of masturbating, learning to masturbate after I slipped on a condom that I had taken from Dad's night stand. It felt so good, sliding the condom on my

penis and then off again. I did it over and over, and the rest is history.

I thought it would be a lot more fun and easier to masturbate out in the desert. There was a place I liked to go hiking in the foothills above the ranch, about a mile from the house.

I rode my bicycle to the bottom of the hill, then hiked up the rest of the way. My dog, Casey, went with me. He liked to chase rabbits while I wandered around.

My special place was hidden in the sand dunes, where I had hiked naked a couple of times. The dunes were surrounded by brush and Joshua trees. It was a secluded place, where I could be alone.

I undid my belt and pants and pushed off my clothes. I was standing up on the dunes totally naked. Showing off my skinny white body, as if the world wanted to see me, I enjoyed being *au naturel* and knew that this would be a good place to masturbate. There was something so sensuous about running my toes through the warm sand. Sliding down the dunes on my bare ass and chasing after the dog was great fun.

I felt so free running over the dunes naked, the wind in my hair and my fuzzy sac flapping between my legs.

After running around awhile, I squatted down to scoop out sand to make a comfortable place to lie in, feeling so carefree as I ran my hands over my body.

Reclining in the warm sand felt nice. I wiggled my buttocks into the sand and buried my feet. From where I lay, I had a good view of the valley below. I got so comfortable that I dozed off. I awoke when the dog barked at a rabbit he was chasing.

Lying naked on the sand in the warm sunshine, gave me a strong sexual urge. This was to be my **first time** doing it in the great outdoors.

My hand gently roamed across my flat stomach and thighs, exploring and searching for my sex. Running my fingers over my pubic mound, the hair curled around my fingers. I noticed that more pubic hair had grown in. My bush was turning into a dark nest of hair.

The sun fell on my glistening pubes and the triangle of curly hair stood out like a beacon against my white thighs. The patch of pubic hair signaled where my sex began. My fingers strayed to play, where my pubic hair bushed out, near the base of my cock.

I pushed some sand up under my balls for support. Leaning back in the sand, I closed my eyes and pretended my hands belonged to Laura, a girl in my school.

I began touching myself and I was getting an erection. As my penis hardened, I pretended that I was reacting to Laura's gentle caresses. My circumcised knob swelled and my nipples hardened. I could not wait for her to touch me some more.

She slowly wrapped her fingers around my cock. Finally, her hand closed around my throbbing penis. Then she began stroking the taut skin back and forth, in a rhythmic motion. It was starting to feel good.

"I will make you come this way. Enjoy yourself," she said. I lay back quietly enjoying her caresses.

Lifting my ass off the sand, my hips danced up and down in rhythm. I thrust my stiff penis up to meet her hand's downward stroke. Then I pulled my penis down when her hand stroked up.

I was starving. Instead of food, I needed pleasure. I knew the simple motion from my hand could fill that hunger. Moving my fingers would bring out a climax and then secret milk.

I yelled out in pleasure. My brain moved my hips and sex into my hand. I was being drugged by pleasure from my own hands.

With my right hand busy on my cock, I was fondling my scrotum with my other hand. Using my fingers, I gently probed the magical contents stored inside.

It was fun learning to masturbate and I was getting better at doing it. By controlling my hand's rhythm, I would almost come, over and over. My hand would speed up and then slow down, going up and down my dick. And squeezing my penis delayed a climax.

Stroking myself almost to an orgasm and then stopping right at the brink. **Oh did that feel good!** I could do this all day long, stroking for pleasure out of doors.

Think of a time like that, one you've remembered all these years. And now let it build for you. Be sure not to use your intellect to recreate it. Allow yourself to experience the emotion, the gut-tingling hunger, the shame if that was part of it. Envision every aspect of the scene, how it affects each of the senses. And now bring your focus to your genitals. How are you—or he, or she—holding your penis? With two fingers? Three? The entire hand?

What are you thinking? Do you like it? Are you apprehensive—or breathing rapidly in anticipation?

Now the hand is moving. What does it feel like? Could you stop it from getting big, even if you wanted to?

You feel the tingle in the pit of your stomach now, don't you? Try to stop it from happening—you can't, can you? You'll be able to years from now, but that's part of what it means to be young, for sex to be new. You're going over the edge, and you can't help yourself. It's happening, happening....

I can imagine a few anally retentive shrinks screeching right now, "pathological regression to infancy! Escapism! Avoidance!" Of course, these same pathetic psychotherapists never raise a finger to protest the tens of thousands of pages of regression that led to masterpieces by Charles Dickens, Herman Hesse, Thomas Wolf, Thomas Mann—just to mention a handful among scores and scores. The substantive difference isn't that they wrote books and we didn't. It is that we are regressing to *sexual* memories and they aren't. It is nothing more than the same old body- and sex-negative prejudice expressing itself in pseudoscientific poppy-cock.

Yes, by all means, make next time the first time—again. But let's not slip into the same quagmire as those who would like to believe that children are asexual. Sex may never have lead to so dramatic a dissolution of our consciousness as when we were adolescents. It may never have so shattered us. But in terms of real fulfillment, it fitted nowhere. It was a slash of light through darkness, and only with maturity and experience can it become a sun, bathing our entire universe in its light and heat.

Chapter Nine

Altered States

The room is small, dimly lit, one flickering candle in each of the corners. In the center a young naked woman stretches across a pile of cushions, the skin taut across her abdomen. Kneeling in a circle around her are four nude men and women, their bodies glistening gold and bronze in the shimmering light.

Repeating softly a slow, rhythmic chant, the participants pass from one to another a large goblet of wine. Each drinks deeply, and the cup is filled many times. No one speaks. There is only the chanting, the wine and, finally, the low moans of increasing desire.

Inevitably, breasts begin to heave in rapid breathing. Phalluses stand erect. Finally, one of the men breaks from the circle and moves slowly toward the passive woman in the center. With great patience he spreads her legs, inserts his organ into her vulva. His glistening buttocks tighten and relax, tighten and relax.

That is no scene from a paperback porn novel. In fact, it's a *worship* service, as sincere and valid as any and more ancient. It's called Tantra, after the name of the gospels or religious books that teach the philosophy. It's adherents call it "a cult of ecstasy focused on a vision of cosmic sexuality."

In a ritual at least 2,000 years old, yet practiced today in hundreds of groups in the United States and Europe, the man impales the motionless woman on the cushions. Often she is a virgin, but the ritual varies. Sometimes a couple reclines on the cushions, and on occasion there is no human at all, only a large, brightly colored painting of the female genitals. Such details vary from group to group.

In the ritual focused on the nude virgin, the first man mounts her with great tenderness. For five minutes, then ten, as the chanting continues, he moves rhythmically. But he is careful not to reach orgasm, for the climax is merely the dessert, not the banquet. Finally, when the man can no longer contain his sexual excitement, he withdraws, and returns to the circle.

Immediately another man takes his place. Thus the ritual continues for many hours, the participants becoming literally drunken with the frenzy of unreleased sexual desire. Yet, only after the last man has mounted the virgin and lifted himself to explosive sexual tension do the worshipers grasp each other and copulate with abandon.

I'll be returning to this scene in chapter ten, because I think its significance as a religious practice—and that is what it is—is the most important thing I will have to say in this book. For now, I want it to serve as a potent example of an altered state of sexual being. Few humans—particularly few males— have the slightest idea what that means.

Let me begin the defining process by comparing it to fantasy—even the most vivid, realistic fantasy. I devoted two chapters in *The Joy of Solo Sex* to that subject, and, if readers' letters are any indication, more men have had more mind-blowing fantasies as a result of those chapters than from any other single source in the history of the world! (That's not much of a statement, of course, considering how few works have been devoted to the creation of sexual fantasies.) The deepest and most intense fantasies can lead to altered states—but the two differ in this critical way:

A fantasy is a drama, even if there's no story line. It takes place in the theatre of the imagination. Perhaps the fantasizer plays a starring role, or perhaps he's in the audience, watching the action while masturbating. He might even be up there on the stage, his face an inch from a performer's phallus, watching the slow and steady stroking, smelling the musky odor of masculinity. But, whatever is happening in fantasy, it is always a performance of some sort.

An altered state, on the other hand, is just what it says—a different way of existing, of seeing and feeling. It's an existence other than from your usual frames of reference. For many people, an altered state, whether achieved through drugs, alcohol, meditation, or sex—is a vacation from the self. That can be the ordinary moral self, or the intellectual, the workaday world, the baggage of interpersonal relationships. We seek out altered states to get away from who we are.

An altered state of sexual being allows us to exist outside of ourselves sexually. In its pure form, an altered state is not a fantasy. It isn't even an orgasm. It is simply an altered dimension of sexual being. But as such, it can be an overwhelmingly satisfying, fulfilling experience.

"Three years ago last spring, I was lying nude on the floor of my bedroom," says Jack L., a businessman in his mid-forties. "I had the patio door open, and a soft breeze washed over my body. It felt like a large tongue gently lapping my abdomen. Then something strange happened. I've never felt it before or since. I felt my guts disappearing.

"It was like I was growing hollow inside—no intestines, no stomach, liver, spleen. I wasn't thinking about it. I was just feeling the hollowness. I started moaning, 'Oh, oh, oh.' Each time I exhaled, I moaned, 'Oh.' My eyes were closed, and I could see myself, my chest, ribs, the hollow abdomen with the navel practically pressing against the spine, the upwardly flowing pubic hair, and there in the center of my body, between my feet and my head, my stone-hard cock."

As Jack explains it, he had no thoughts. He had no sexual fantasies, was not thinking in terms of orgasm. He was absorbed completely in the feeling and image of hollowness.

"Maybe it's masochistic—I don't know," he says, "but the idea of being just a shell existing for no other purpose than to support a cock was just overwhelming. The more I breathed and chanted and let go the deeper into it I got and the better I felt. I don't know where I went that day, but I sure as hell wasn't in that room."

Jack insists on two things: 1) The altered state that he experienced was definitely and deeply sexual; 2) He did not have, and did not wish to have, an orgasm. That illustrates an important concept that is, unfortunately, foreign to most western thinking: Sex needn't be orgasmic to be satisfying.

Jack's experience illustrates the four essentials of an altered state of being. They are:

—Deep, relaxed, sleep-like breathing
—Ritual sounds or chants
—Hypnotic image focusing
—Dissociation

Breathing

How you breathe dramatically effects the way your body —including your brain—works. You may recall that silly thing we did as children; we would hyperventilate, breathing in rapid pants almost like a dog, then blowing hard, as though playing a trumpet, but not allowing any air to escape. Susceptible youngsters promptly passed out. And we thought that was fun!

Hyperventilating saturates the blood—and therefore the organs, including the brain—with oxygen. Among some people, that oxygen rush can produce anxiety, which is why that condition can be treated by breathing into and out of a paper bag—the re-used air contains less oxygen. The way you breathe can affect your sex life. According to sex therapist Lana A. Clark, Ph.D., proper breathing can overcome a great many sex problems. She says, "The body's basic urge is to surrender completely to sexual impulse, while the mind is unwilling to release control and be carried along, unresisting. Orgasm is often described as a 'drop into the unknown.' It is a spontaneous experience. The conscious mind can surrender and allow it to happen, but can not cause it. Many people fear the temporary loss of ego, identity, and boundaries that accompanies orgasm."

What does that have to do with breathing? Doctor Parks says that most people tense their bodies as they approach orgasm, and unconsciously stop or control their breathing, "afraid to allow the rippling spread of the orgasmic response throughout the entire body." Her solution is "breathing deeply and regularly to completely oxygenate the brain."

If you feel any tension in your body, you can make a wonderful breathing experiment that will help you to relax. When we're asleep, most of us breathe in a very distinct pattern: We take a quick shallow breath, then exhale at length. The rhythm goes like this: Oh *yeess*, oh *yeess*. Try breathing that way now. If you haven't done it before, it will be awkward at first. You'll think you can't get enough air in the "oh" inhale to carry you through the "*yeess*." But of course, since that's how we breathe when we're asleep, we get plenty of oxygen this way.

Do it just long enough to prove the point, which is that breathing in a certain way can help you to relax and perhaps feel a bit sleepy. I'd like you to finish this chapter before actually dozing off!

To awaken the body, as is needed to achieve altered states, we reverse the breathing pattern of sleep. That is, we inhale fully and at length, then breath out quickly: "Yeess, *oh*! Yeess, *oh*!" Many of us breathe this way naturally, but if you don't, you'll want to practice so that eventually it becomes natural and you don't have to think about it. Regardless of the claims and disclaimers made by various practitioners of altered sexual states, all these breathing techniques work for the same reason: They saturate the brain with oxygen, which, in theory at least, makes it more alert and sensitive.

Ritual Chant

Altered states, when mentally rather than chemically induced, are actually a form of autosuggestion, or self-hypnosis. And, as everyone who has ever seen any of those old-time mystery movies knows, a monotonous rhythm helps to induce susceptibility to hypnotic suggestion. Whether it's the ticking of the metronome, the gentle, rhythmic swaying of a pocket watch on its chain, or the tapping of fingers on a desk, predictable repetition seems to whittle away at our defenses.

For literally thousands of years, altered sexual states have been induced in part by the monotonous rhythm of ritual chants, from "ooohm," to "huh!" and "yes!" (In fact, these spontaneous chants provide fertile material for psychological research. Moments before orgasm, I have heard men chanting, some in whispers, some in shouts, "No, Mommie! No, Mommie!" "Dear God, Dear God," "My cock!" and many similar expressions.)

Try not to plan intellectually what it is that you will chant. Better to make a spontaneous sound that has no meaning than to allow the intellect to slip in through the back door and short circuit your efforts at *being*. Remember, that is the goal—not thinking, or doing, but simply *being*.

Hypnotic Image

Steve Largent of the Seattle Seahawks is one of the greatest pass receivers of all time. He recently told an interviewer, "I guarantee you I can go out here right now and you can throw me ten balls... I could quit watching the ball half way to me. Once I have the line of where you threw the ball, I can close my eyes and catch most of them." There's a kind of visualizing that goes on, and it goes on without the aid of the intellect. An alligator can leap four feet into the air and catch a bird in flight, and the animal does it the same way Largent catches passes with his eyes closed—he uses not the neocortical but the limbic part of his brain, the primitive seat of passion. That's where we must reach if we're to experience an altered sexual state.

We focus not on an activity—which is fantasy—but an object.

Ralph Walker of *The Loving Brotherhood* wrote a while back to tell me of just such an experience which he had at age eleven. In his imagination, he had focused on a girl his age. She was in the woods and simply standing there naked, allowing him to observe her. He focused so intensely that he was transported—you might call it an out-of-body experience—to the woods. And he was so enraptured and inspired by the girl that he had a spontaneous orgasm.

Probably the most common image for men, both straight and gay, is the male phallus. One man described his Ideal Cock as follows: "It is eight inches long, five inches circumference. When fully erect, it would rise in awesome majesty, running wet all over with a copious flow of pre-ejaculatory fluid. It would gracefully curve inward, with the tip just touching my belly at the navel....

"This wonder-cock would begin throbbing in time with my pounding pulse, and in five or ten minutes, even if I hadn't touched it, it would succumb to its own throbbing and shoot a gigantic ejaculation all over my belly....An erection like that, whether standing in front of my wife or in front of my reflection in the mirror represents the ultimate compliment or salute, as if to say, 'Here, you see this? This is how much you turn me on. This hard! This high! Up as far as it can possibly go! This flood of semen! This is what you do to me!'"

Whether the image is a cock, a nude girl, a buttocks or whatever, fix your concentration on that exclusively. Allow it to become real for you. Let it absorb your being and fill you completely.

Dissociation

A couple of years back, a reader wrote to a sexual advice columnist, "Once in a while when I'm outrageously excited I seem to lose my sense of self and can't be sure whether I am the man or the woman, my partner or myself. It's as if I'm fucking and being fucked, getting and receiving at the same time. I love this incredible exhilarating experience, but what does it mean?"

It means, of course, that this man is experiencing an altered sexual state. He is *dissociating*, or stepping out of the person he normally is. In western psychology, dissociating unintentionally and uncontrollably is an emotional disorder. Victims might be found wandering around not knowing how they got there—or who they are.

We're not talking about dissociation in that sense. As sex therapist William A. Henkin explained in his column, "As long as you have a good sense of self to begin with, and can control the times and places you dissociate and the way you regain your boundaries, the experience can be fun." As Henkin observes, dissociating has "a parallel" in many shamanic traditions where magicians seek to leave their bodies in order to visit the spirit realms in the course of specific rituals. And the sort of merging you enjoy is a highly-valued goal in some tantric disciplines."

A few years ago, in a column for *CELEBRATE The Self Newsletter*, I tried to show both straight and gay men how, by dissociation, they could have an orgasmic sexual experience as a woman. Now, although no one actually wrote to object, it must be assumed that ninety percent of men who read that column had no desire to identify as a woman. Perhaps only ten percent, like me, are trisexuals—they'll try anything once. Keep in mind that this was a fantasy experience, not an altered state fixing on a single image, but I think it illustrates well what goes on in the dissociation process. Here are the instructions I gave:

Lie down nude with your head slightly raised on a pillow. Begin breathing deeply and slightly more rapidly than usual. The goal is to hyperoxygenate the blood, which leads to more alertness and sensitivity. (If you find yourself getting light-headed, return to normal breathing.) Envision your own ideal man. Perhaps he's gentle and handsome, perhaps a raging stallion. Perhaps he's you. See him naked and aroused, and study every part of his body. He's panting with desire for a woman. You understand how he feels, his aching need for release. You want nothing for yourself, only to make him happy, relieve him of this torturous hunger. To fulfill him, you must transform yourself into a woman.

Both of you know that you can do it. For this man's pleasure, you will sacrifice your manhood, selflessly surrender your phallus, watch his eyes brighten as they gaze upon your body, feel his warm, strong hands plying your breasts.

Let it happen. see how beautiful you are in his eyes, what hunger and passion he brings to you. Let his passion and pleasure fulfill you. Feel his lips on your neck, his hot breath against your cheek. With arms clasped around you, he holds you to him, penetrating you. Does he kiss your face tenderly, moving slowly? Is he a ravager, mindless in his hunger? Feel how warm, safe, and fulfilled you are beneath him. You love the power of his sweat-drenched chest against your breasts, and, as he moves in and out of you, your own passion builds. You ignore everything else, just surrender to this glow. You feel it spreading.

Do you move in rhythm with this man who has taken you, increasing the friction, rising quickly? Or do you lie in absolute passivity, letting the glow build until it overwhelms you?

He reached down, touches you between your legs. You feel his fingers moving gently, back and forth. His lips suck at your throat, your breasts. You can hear the sucking sound, feel his saliva, the heat of his face.

155

His breathing grows rapid. Rising up on his elbows, gasping, he thrusts in long, powerful strokes. Your eyes meet. You see his overflowing pleasure. He fills you with ecstasy. You are swept up in him.

I want to close this chapter with an account of an altered sexual state written by Dick Phelps. It has all the ingredients we've discussed thus far—focus on an image (the cock), ritual, proper breathing, and dissociation. But it has another element as well, transcendence into a spiritual realm, and for that reason it serves as a perfect transition into the next and final chapter.

When I was about fourteen and cruising through the public library of my home town, I came across a book by Evelyn Underhill called *Mysticism*. I checked the book out, hoping it would explain how to make oneself invisible or perhaps even how to levitate. Instead, I found a complete guide to meditative life.

That little volume changed my entire life, perhaps more than any other single book I have ever studied.

Evening after evening I would secrete myself alone in my room and practice what I thought to be meditation. I still wasn't sure how the meditative experience was supposed to enlighten one, and actually expected to see flashing lights along with levitation without the encumbrance of the physical body, as well as other mysterious and adventurous experiences.

My experiments had to be secret. My family already thought I was overly reclusive, due mostly to my early secret addiction to solo sex, and so any experiments with meditation might have prompted them to seek some sort of psychiatric care for me. I was really discovering a variety of *hot* ways to get myself off. My loving but uninformed grandmother caught me once and warned me that if I kept it up (no pun intended) I would undoubtedly have to have it cut off as well as go crazy—specifically she warned that I would have to have it cut off to *keep* from going crazy. Her warning only made me more secretive as well as sick with worry.

In my room alone, I would sit on my bed in what I thought to be the correct Lotus position with my eyes dreamily closed, practicing my interpretation of meditation and attempting to force a result.

I muddled through my version of the meditation exercise at least once every day and the only thing that would ever happen was that I would get a raging hard-on, demanding my undivided attention—which meant beating myself off all the way across the finish line. Even by mustering all the *will power* within me, I was unable to control my eager teenage dick.

This practice deepened the frustration and disappointment which plagued my efforts at meditation. My attempts only seemed to result in logging more jack-off time, which brought me to the edge of giving up the meditation. Meditation seemed only to intensify my desire for the insatiable "unclean habit" and its inexorable, dire, and shameful results. Even then I suspected that all those warnings were "hog wash," but the guilt remained and I thought that in all the world I was the only boy completely "hooked" and unable to stop!

Still, my daily "meditation" sessions, in the safe, secret, candle-lit quiet of my bedroom, became my main pursuit. Almost immediately, during meditations, my cock would stiffen up and begin to throb and juice away. Being unable to stand it another second, I would guiltily begin to fondle myself to orgasm. Only then could I settle down for a serious meditation.

It finally got so that I would harden up even before I began meditating, but by then I could hold off my fondle time for an hour or so and just lie there, letting myself "go with the flow," and little by little my cock began to jerk by itself. I was less and less aware of my body but more and more aware of my cock's spasms.

I just relaxed and let it happen. I concentrated on nothingness, still hoping for a glimpse of those flashing lights or at least an out-of-body experience.

Well, the lights started flashing and I must have been out of my body because all I was conscious of was my jerking *dick*. I became less and less aware of my body and my cock became my entire being. All I could feel was my jerking cock. *The entire universe was concentrated in my cock, and there was nothing else anywhere.*

I became my cock and it was jerking me. I was helpless. My cock and I were one, I was the jerker as well as the jerkee.

Suddenly I could feel my semen jetting out all over me as I sailed through the universe, unsupported and free. Not a single thought entered my mind other than the exquisite beauty of the orgasm I was experiencing. My entire body was hypnotized and totally rigid. I was in an upward arch, supported by the back of my head and the heels of my feet, my cock shooting toward the ceiling. Yet, I was perfectly comfortable, just as though I were pressed firmly against my mattress.

My mind was totally in the head of my cock. I *was* my cock, and that's all I was, a free-floating, bodiless, jerking cock.

During the span of the orgasm, I ardently hoped that I would be locked in that consciousness forever, with no escape possible.

That was, for me, a truly religious experience, on that great sea of nothingness, alone with God and the universe. It has continued to be over and over and

over, throughout the many years since that first unex-
pected, almost frightening event. For me, even today,
it's a very special religious celebration. Maybe that's
how a good meditation should be!

Chapter Ten

The Mystic Experience
Sex and God

Don is in his early sixties now. I've never actually met him, but I felt that we were soul brothers from the moment I read in a letter from him to me, "You really hit a strong resonant chord in me. I have never been able to talk to anyone about some of these things. When I have tried, on occasion, they shook their heads, and said I was weird."

Don was talking specifically about my views on finding God through the body. And, like Don, some have thought me "weird" for linking sex and God. (Note, I did not say sex and religion. I have little patience with religion, by which I mean an organized business established and maintained by human beings.) But if you're talking about that which transcends the material, how can you *not* be talking about sex? I've met only a few people who epitomize erotic spirituality as much as Don, and so I'm going to quote him at length:

> I remember when I was a small boy and my family had just moved from Hawaii to Richmond, California, on the shore of San Francisco Bay. My dad took me by the hand and lead me over some hills near town to where there was a creek. He had grown up in

161

Richmond and he had played in that same creek when he was a boy. On a summer day, there were swimming holes full of naked boys. On that first day some boys invited us in to swim with them—and we did. My Dad showed me all the best trees for climbing, the trees that had the best limbs for bouncing on, and all the best places to be.

As I grew older, I spent a lot of time naked near the creek in company with other boys. It was usually just play, but when things got tough and I had to go somewhere and think, that is where I went. Sometimes I would sit there naked and alone and think.

There was a lot of isolated space in those days (I'm talking about the 1930's and early 1940's). Sometimes a bunch of us would go to a beach on the bay and swim, naked of course, and even play ball naked. It's just the way I grew up.

I didn't really care if anyone came by and saw me naked, so long as it wasn't a policeman. I was quite a bit more open than most boys that way, possibly because of my beginnings in Hawaii. I would undress in front of total strangers at times, which my friends were reluctant to do. For example, one day two of my friends and I rode our bicycles out to an old pier that was falling to pieces in the bay. Off shore a ways a few porpoises were swimming. I had heard of "boy on a dolphin." Why not "boy on a porpoise?" There were maybe a half dozen old codgers fishing off the pier, and their eyes widened as I stripped naked and dove into the water.

I have always been a strong swimmer, and in a while I got to where the porpoises were. Suddenly there was a splash. I didn't know porpoises were *that* big! I swam back and one of the old men gave me a hand getting back on the pier. I stood there drying off and telling them about how startled I was. What I saw in their eyes was amusement at my temerity in standing naked before strangers, but, *much* more than that, I saw nostalgia. They no doubt remembered when they, too, were young, smooth, lean and beautiful, and full of pep.

In the Oregon cascades there are a lot of lakes. There are some wilderness areas. And back-packing and camping are very popular—so much so that the number of campers is not limited by a permit system. In that area, casual nudity is taken for granted. No one pays any attention. Someone may walk up to you and talk to you while you are naked. Usually they won't. Technically, it's illegal but there is no one to enforce the law up there. The common attitude seems to be, "If you don't like it, don't look."

When I was a little boy, the Hawaiian religion was practiced to some extent. (It was totally illegal in those days.) It is only very recently that native religions have been legal in the land of the free.

One of my very earliest memories was of a ritual shark killing. The one to do the act, probably a teenager, looked like a powerful, big man to me. He stood on a rock naked and shouted his prayers. Then he swam, with a knife in his hand, to where a great white shark, a man-eater, was circling near the shore. The water boiled briefly, then he swam back, stood up once again naked in front of everyone, and shouted his prayers again.

Nudity was common in the 1930's in Hawaii. Most kids ran around naked most of the time. There were also religious obligations to be nude at certain times.

Now, I may be wrong. But as I recall, things created by gods are sacred, those made by man are profane. It is not proper to have anything profane come between you and the gods. Clothing is made by man. So we ought to take them off when face to face with a god.

This was particularly necessary when one chanced to meet the Goddess Pele. She was said to be greatly offended if one did not show Her proper respect. And if you offend Pele there will be fires, the volcano could erupt, and it could be bad. I do not recall ever seeing anyone disrobe believing themselves to be in the presence of a god, but that is the way the religion was.

I spoke of a creek near Richmond, Ca. Near the creek, on the side of the hill toward town, was a tall rock spire which we called Pinnacle Rock. We boys liked to climb it sometimes. I don't know how I got the idea, but I thought it would be an act of worship, an act of homage to the God or Gods, if I watched the full moon rise while standing naked on top of Pinnacle Rock. I finally did it. I stripped at the base of the rock. I climbed to the top and stood with my arms upraised while the gorgeous full moon rose over the hill. I don't know if anyone saw me. All I know is that I felt almost ecstatic afterwards. To me it was a holy experience.

One of the most shaking religious experiences I ever had in my life occurred when I decided to sleep In a Native American spirit circle...I fasted three days, then traveled by bicycle to the coast, about 65 miles, hid my bike, walked to the circle (which I had found on a previous trip), and prepared to spend the night. When I judged it was time, I stripped, and, taking a single blanket, stepped into the circle. I lay down, I stood up, I was restless. Then, as the sun set into the Pacific, I made up a little prayer.

The night seemed endless at first, but then I did dream. I did not have the 'separate reality' experience of the shaman. But I did have very vivid and memorable dreams. The spirits did speak to me! In the morning I faced the east and, as the sun rose, I gave thanks to the spirits. The message I got was very personal and secret. The experience was extremely meaningful; in fact I would say it changed my life.

I feel certain that the Native American Gods are real. They have spoken to me! My experience as a 16-year-old on Pinnacle Rock was incredibly moving. The Pagan Gods are real.

The point I want to stress here is that the sacredness of Don's experience is body-centered. He talks about his father introducing him to nakedness in the out-of-doors, of sharing that out-flowing of nakedness with strangers, with nature, and finally with God. In each case, there are overtones of the sensual, the erotic. It is precisely what Robert Bahr means when he talks about "Celebrating the Bodyspirit."

That in itself is ecstasy, and it is so far ahead of where most people in the United States are emotionally that it must seem weird and downright radical from their perspective. But I want to explore something even *more* radical, and I discussed it briefly in the previous chapter. I want to talk about the oldest and most popular religion in human history—*sexual worship*. Regarding virtually all ancient religions, according to anthropologist George Ryley Scott, "The androgynous creative deity was best supplicated or propitiated by offerings concerned with the pleasures of the flesh. In such circumstances, to the worshiper as to the gods, licentiousness was not a sin: on the contrary, it was a duty."

The ancient Greeks made of the goddess Aphrodite's temple a bordello, supplying it with literally thousands of the nation's most beautiful women. Their responsibility was to bring complete sexual joy to strangers—both men and women—visiting the city. The visitors paid handsomely for the chance to worship in Aphrodite's temple—and many became converts.

The Bacchantes, Greek worshipers of the sun god Bacchus, revelled in even greater sexual abandon. According to one description, "In the spring of the year, on nights of the full moon, they (the worshipers) retired to the hills behind Athens to give themselves over to the mysteries of the gods. They drank drugged wine and danced naked around a large phallus representing the god's potency."

In Rome, phallic statues protected gardens and houses, blacksmith's shops and people. Scott writes, "The ancient Romans, almost without exception, wore in plain view, on their persons, amulets and charms of phallic form; and when marching into battle the soldiers carried on their standards similar phallic symbols. Even children had phallic emblems hung upon their bodies and attached to their dress.... So widespread were these practices that there is scarcely a nation of antiquity whose herald did not show many examples of depictions of both the male and female genitalia."

At one time, every young Roman girl could expect to sacrifice her virginity not to the warm, throbbing penis of the man she loved, but to the hard, cold stone phallus of a god. Following an elaborate ritual, she would climb nude into the sculptured lap and impale herself upon the huge, erect penis until the pain and blood signified that her hymen had been pierced. In some cultures a priest charged a fee to take the virgin's first fruits on behalf of the deity.

Even the Christian church has found itself in continuous battle against the impulse to combine sex with worship. Saint Paul was constantly haranguing the pagans-turned-Christians to cease sex orgies as part of their worship. Two thousand years earlier, Moses smashed the tablets containing the ten commandments in violent anger upon discovering that, in his absence, the Jews, too, had begun practicing sex worship.

In a previous chapter, I introduced Tantra as the epitome of an erotic religion. What sets Tantra apart is that, while some religions use sexual ecstacy to trigger spiritual ecstacy, Tantra sees sex and the sex organs as sacred in themselves. And that's why it's one of the most persecuted religions in history.

Many of the earliest Tantric gospels were destroyed by Hindu zealots and a succession of invaders who conquered India. Today, only a handful of the original Tantric gospels remain. Monasteries where Tantric truths were taught were razed, the libraries burned, monks and worshipers slain.

From the beginning, Tantra was a philosophy of rebellion. It flagrantly disregarded the tenets of society, flaunting nudism in the face of prissiness, confronting body shame with sexual freedom. Even in ancient times—perhaps from Zoroaster—men (much more frequently than women) have declared war against their own natural sexuality, so the tantrikas (Tantra worshipers) made sexuality the major battlefield. In fact, they went so far as to declare that, in their secret rituals, they even had cosmic coitus with demons and goddesses. The tantrikas simply believed that life should be completely free from restraint.

So firmly did the tantrika believe that pleasure and not regulation was the function of religion that one of the sacred gospels contains this story: A wise sage who had spent his whole life in devotion to a Tantric goddess was granted as a reward a chance to actually visit the Hindu deity Vishnu. After a long journey, he comes upon the god. No noble, clear-eyed, thundering Jehovah, this Vishnu. Instead, he lolls casually upon his cushions, his eyes drooping and reddened with wine. Surrounding him are beautiful girls, some clothed, others naked, all embracing in passion and ecstasy.

The god himself staggers drunkenly from one girl to the next, enjoying each of them any way he wishes.

The old sage is puzzled and disappointed. He asks why a god should behave like this when he has always felt religion meant restraint. He is told that his views of religion are of an inferior and undeveloped character. The highest rites are those he now witnesses, with wine and sexual intercourse and meat eating.

For hundreds of years, Tantra continued to evolve, and by the sixth century AD it had become a more formal and organized religion. A complete set of Tantras (gospels) had been compiled and a "history" of Tantra had been invented.

The supreme divinity is a female being. She is composed of two influences, the tranquil *shiva* (female) and the dynamic power *shakti* (the male). Only when they are coupled in sexual ecstasy is there completeness and meaning in the universe.

But the tantrika's concept of godhood is a far cry from that of the western world. Men and women can themselves become truly divine simply by imitating the two forms of the great Being and uniting in supreme sexual bliss.

When the man's lingam, as the Indians called the penis, is inserted into the woman's yoni, both soar above society's moral and social limitations.

"What is evil to the ordinary man is salvation to the tantrika," according to the sacred writings.

A major Tantra tenet is that all males are merely one form of expression of the omnipresent female goddess. Thus, even Krisna, the handsome god with whom all women fall helplessly in love, is actually a form assumed by the goddess Nityā. To symbolize that, some male tantrikas actually dress like girls.

Although always controversial, Tantra by the ninth century had a strong following among the masses and enormous temples were built to accommodate the erotic rituals. The facades of those temples are famous throughout the world today, not only for their erotic subject matter but for the startling artistry of their execution. The figures were intended simply and frankly to stimulate sexual desire in those observing them. Finely detailed and exaggerated are the aspects that would trigger sexual response. Says Philip Rawson in his book, *Erotic Art of the East*:

"Breasts, usually, are of an opulent fullness, as they are so often on Indian girls of the true 'goddess' age of 16.... Navels may be deep-set, spines have a charming channel, necks lined with creases that reveal the softness of feminine subcutaneous fat... Finally, the feminine vulva is by the Apsarases freely offered to view, as a beauty with an expression of its own. The clitoris is much in evidence, but rarely the labia minora. In Orissa, for example, the vulva's openness proclaims the eager nature of the Apsaras."

Adds Rawson, "The postures adopted by the sculptured girls are all those which are best calculated to display the sexual qualities of their figures. Twisted postures with an outthrust hip, or with lifted breasts, hollowed back and salient behind are very common."

The figures run the gamut of sexual activity, and few modern libertines have experienced a sex act that hasn't been depicted in vivid detail on those Hindu temple facades. Men and women gleefully masturbate. Penises plug every orifice—mouths, anuses, vaginas. Full-breasted women accommodate two or more men simultaneously. One man, using hands, toes and penis, brings obvious joy to several women.

Inside the temple, some worshipers knelt naked before the shrine of the great female Being, the icon representing the goddess often simply a giant vulva.

Others, those who sought more power, worshipped the sculpture of an erect male penis. In some Tantric temples these lingual icons are the most common religious objects. In others, male tantrikas worshipped their own erect penises, playing and singing chants to them and handling them with utter reverence.

Even today, while Hindu Tantric rites involve ecstatic, orgastic sex, the rituals in no way resemble an ordinary swinger's party. The mood is solemn, with flickering candles, incense, tinkling bells, magic, incantations, wands and spells, secret words and postures.

Eventually Buddhists began adopting some Tantric teachings, modifying them to conform to some of their more puritanical views. One change was that the Buddhists strictly prohibited the spilling of semen.

Drawing on the ancient Greek belief that the soul is contained in ejaculatory fluid, the Buddhist tantrikas taught that the man who allowed his sperm to leave his body literally weakened his spiritual strength. So, in a radical break with the Hindus, the Buddhists prohibited ejaculation. They taught that Nirvana, not pleasure, was the goal, and although that required sexual union through coitus, the act was not to be enjoyed. The copulator was to strive for higher and higher desire, so much so that his face flushed radiantly with blood. Still, he was to deny himself eternally the fulfillment of orgasm.

A peculiar practice that grew out of that attitude was called *vagroli,* or "return of the semen." One historian, Alexandra David-Neel, describes it as follows:

"A certain class of Tibetan occultists [who also practiced *vagroli*] teach a mode of training that is half physical and half psychic, comprising such strange practices as causing a return into the body of the seminal fluid, or reabsorbing it when it has actually been ejected."

Unlikely as it sounds, after many years of practice, some men actually claimed the ability to contract some of the ejaculated sperm back up through the urethra. Concludes Robert S. DeRopp in his book *Sex Energy.* "It remains merely a trick and one, moreover, that can lead to infection of the bladder by the introduction of microorganisms from the vagina."

Today, where Tantra still exists, social and legal pressures have done much to enforce the Buddhic version in place of the Hindu. In some instances, a strong puritanism has sprung up within the movement itself—ironic, since Tantra was originally a reaction to puritanism in the first place. These tantrikas deny that overt sex was ever practiced, insisting that the gospels and the temple sculptures and all other overt sexual references were simply symbolic.

Yet, the original Tantra, the ecstasy of sex, still exists underground throughout India, Europe and America.

I'm going to make a radical proposal now. If religion as you have known it all your life leaves you unfulfilled, if it seems to be, at least as humans have interpreted it, a deception—consider a religion centered in the body and its sexuality.

Now, any meaningful religion would have to meet certain criteria. They're as follows:

1. Comfort in the Face of Death

I want to go deeper. I want to tell you a story that will shock you. I hope it will make you think as well. I was in my mid-twenties and living in the Pocono Mountains of Pennsylvania with my first wife. I was not yet mature enough to know that I was bisexual. I thought the attraction I felt for Johnny Copenhaver was a passionate but purely Platonic friendship. We had great fun together, leaving our wives at home to gossip while we caroused all over the Poconos.

Then, one winter night, I received a phone call. Johnny, who had separated from his wife and children and had moved into the air-tight basement of a house he was building, was dead. The flames on his gas heater had somehow gone out. Perhaps he had put them out himself—I can't be sure. He had died of gas inhalation.

A couple of years later I finally found the strength to visit his grave. It was in a cemetery at the top of a hill overlooking the Delaware River and the highway below. There, on a spring day, hidden from view by Johnny's headstone, I had my only orgasm with him.

If that sounds uncommon, unjustifiable, I have a surprise for you. Hugh Russell wrote this to me not long ago: "I walk slowly around the garden, stroking my stiff dick, looking for another spot. I'm drawn to Charles' stone in the garden wall, carved with his name and dates, center piece of the tea ceremony in his memory last week. I sit on it, stroking very gently. Feeling the heat and energy rise up from the stone to my asshole. I haven't yet come on the stone, but I know it's the way to feel more of a connection to Charles. I ask myself, 'Why not this morning?' I turn around, hold my cock over the middle and stroke, slowly, unhurriedly, feeling the energy slowly build, watching the shadow of my arm and cock on the stone. I get down on my knees on the stone. Energy rises, and then rises some more. 'I love you, Charles, I love you.' and the come shoots all over the stone. In a minute I bend over and kiss the stone, and slowly get to my feet, leaving the come to dry on the stone."

I understand the mind of the Christian fundamentalist, and, to him or her, the thought of someone masturbating on a grave is most likely reprehensible. But why? *Why*? Sex and death are inextricably linked in our psyche. It's my guess that every man has experienced that connection in one way or another—perhaps fantasizing his own death at orgasm, recognizing that sex alone, apart from religion, can make even death tolerable.

The French actually call sex "the little death."

Anecdotally, I must have a mountain of stories illustrating the power of sex over death. A man and woman were found dead of smoke inhalation in the basement of a burned-out building. They were nude, and died in the act of copulation. Theodore Reich has written that, before entering battle during the second world war, young men would masturbate ten times. The orgasm calmed their fears.

Reich argues, in fact, (*in Masochism and Modern Man*) that the very act of suffering masochistically is, in some cases, symbolic death in the midst of which sex triumphs in ecstatic orgasm.

2. Completeness and Contentment

The typical fundamentalist talks about having found happiness, joy, and a host of additional qualities as a result of conversion—but I can assure you, both as a former fundamentalist and as a pastor, that there is often less contentment and more downright misery among born-again Christians than in the general population. A very obvious reason is that the demands of fundamentalism run contrary to those required for emotional normalcy. For example, fundamentalists condemn lust, solo sex, the flesh. They celebrate crucifying the self, denying the self, condemning the self. They extol being meek, a doormat, commanded to serve others and give all that they have to the poor. No one could live that sort of life. It's completely out of touch with human nature. It's like beating a horse because he can't fly, beating him until he says, "Of course I can fly. I *am* flying," in spite of the truth. And that, my friends, isn't emotionally healthy.

Sex really *does* bring contentment, relaxing both mind and body. It is a contentment that feels right and normal, in harmony with the universe. Only those afflicted with neurotic religious shame feel anything but peace and tranquillity after sex.

3. A More Positive Relationship To Others

Richard Moss, writing in *The Black Butterfly*, says, "Often I find that I am having 'sex' merely by being in the presence of certain people. It no longer matters whether they are male or female, what they look like, how they live, what they do.... I am always 'making love' with those around me in accordance with their capacity to enter energetic rapport. It does not require words or even knowing one another."

I call that experience *the extended self*. Think of it: at every moment there's a universal nonspecific orgy going on between you and all other beings. Look out your window. See that man or woman? You are united in reality, and reality is erotic. We are all potential lovers, our flesh united.

I will do what I can to make your life easier because, through erotic reality, we are lovers. Not in the literal sense, as Richard Moss points out, but in the potentially literal and clearly figurative sense. The day I recognized that fact, I couldn't help smiling at people as I walked down the street. Several smiled back. A few said hello. Most turned away nervously. But how good it felt, this feeling that everyone I met had been a lover, had shared my body, my most intimate and vulnerable moments, and I had shared theirs.

Somehow, that seems to be a firmer basis for loving your neighbor and caring for him or her than some vague promise of heavenly rewards that appeal to your selfish greed.

4. Connecting With God

People just never shut up when it comes to God. No two of them ever agree, *yet everyone has all the answers.* In the entire universe, no subject has claimed more experts than God.

Apart from what others have told us—verbally and in books—what do we *know* about God?

—We know that "God" is a man-made word, that God doesn't call himself—or herself, or itself—God. Without blaspheming, we can say that "God" is a harsh, guttural word, not nearly as pretty as "allure," "serenity," and "allegorical." Any other word would do as well as God if we all agreed on its meaning. So, from now on, I will not use the word God. Instead, I will call that idea *The Other.*

—*The Other* is not limited to the masculine gender. I have great respect for most people's opinions, but anyone who thinks *The Other* is a man is a shallow thinker. The same is true of those who think she is a woman. My god, we're talking about *T.O.*! By definition *all* genders are manifested in this Being. If *The Other* is omniscient, omnipotent, and omnipresent, all things are embodied in *T.O.* including both male and female gender identity, along with pansexual passion.

—*The Other* begins where our ability to comprehend ends. *If I can conceive The Other, it is not The Other! This* is what it means to be human. *That* is what it means to be *The Other.* (This insight from Taoism.)

—No person has seen *The Other* at any time. It's an Old Testament concept; to look upon the face of God directly would lead to instant death. (The exceptions, of course, are fundamentalist evangelists such as Oral Roberts, who met face to face with Jesus Christ as part of a fund-raising drive.)

—We know that the Judeo-Christian god, as he's presented by those in the religion business, doesn't win any blue ribbons as a role model for good behavior. He's a petty, jealous, relatively impotent bully who lays down all sorts of arbitrary rules, orders his people from time to time to break virtually every one of his own commandments, and gets his poor followers into all sorts of messes. He even "repents" having made humankind. So much for foreknowledge.

In the New Testament, we discover the greatest catch 22 in all history: render your entire life to Jesus, virtually die to this world on the gamble that there is, in fact, an afterlife, and if there is a heaven, you'll go there. But should you turn down this golden chance to live the life of a catatonic, should you choose to celebrate your body and rejoice in the fullness of your pleasure, you'll sit your ass in hell, baby!

What can we *know* about *The Other*? Even to pose the question is to rely on the *intellectual*, the newest, least developed aspect of the human brain. It is with my *primal* sources of knowledge, those with which we slithered through the mud and climbed trees a million years before the first man thought of god—it is through those senses that *The Other* can be felt. We can know, if not much, at least something.

—We know at times that we can feel *T.O.*'s presence—when we walk naked through a forest, gaze in peace at a star-filled sky, hold our infant son/daughter in our arms, look into the eyes of someone we love so deeply that even we who are linguistic assembly lines have no words for it, share intimately in touch or conversation with our dearest friends, feel the splintering of our self-control, our self-consciousness, our very selves in the explosive ecstasy of orgasm.

We can know *ardor*—the fervor, the zeal, the burning heat of life. Saint Iraeneus, a second century Christian martyr, said, "The glory of God is man fully alive." In nature, in bed, walking the streets of a strange city alone, we are taken with a satori, and without reasonable explanation a surge of passion

175

moves through us and we are enthralled by life. Unexplainable joy takes hold of us and we smile and feel at one with others and with *The Other*.

There is no self then, no ego, no necessity to condemn others. They search in their own ways for *T.O.* We have found *one* way to the truth and the life, not the only way.

I mentioned reaching to *The Other* through orgasm. As psychoanalyst Eugene Monik puts it in *Ecstasy Journal*, "Sexuality, seen in this light, is a means of experiencing cosmos. Sexuality, as 'an autonomous mode of cognition' [knowledge], is a way into the mystery of creation, of approaching and participating in the god-image. Eliade seems to suggest that sexuality is more than a way. It may be *the* way. Human beings connect with the deeper aspects of themselves through their sexual, sensual, orgasmic, instinctual experience."

Does all this mean that there is no truth to Christianity, or Judaism, or Islam, or Buddha or other religions? Are we to give up our faith and face life hopeless and in despair? It means nothing of the kind. Again by definition, every object of religious faith is a metaphor. We need something we *can* understand, a touchstone, a model, of that which is beyond our capacity to conceive—*T.O.* As long as we cling to the body and emotional truths of our metaphors, we can live "safe in the arms of Jesus," love our neighbors as ourselves, and love ourselves in others—truly the basis of all morality. But when we mistake our *metaphor* for the ultimate truth of *The Other* itself, condemning to eternal hell our brother for having sex this way instead of that, looking at these magazines instead of those, when we condemn kissing ass in passion instead of in greed, then it is we who are damned to self-deceit and inhumanity.

That's why fundamentalist Christianity is already dead. The corpses of its passing are sprinkled all over the sidewalk, amid the blood and needles and fetuses in every city of the country. The *religion* is sterile and impotent. But don't confuse that with the teachings of Jesus. It is not Jesus' fault. It was the fault of those who created a religion, and stuck his name on it, and tossed the teachings aside.

In his powerful novel *The Good Conscience*, Carlos Fuentes tells the story of Jamie, newly pubescent, intoxicated with the sensuality of a life in which candles are virile, flower baskets brim with "daisies and jasmine, roses and blue dahlias, lilies, drowsy poppies, solemn canna lilies and playful carnations;" the smell of "the hot sexuality of the stallion...the high buttocks of the Indian woman, the little breasts of the young girls..."

Jamie runs along a dirty street, his shirt open, his sleeves rolled up. He enters a church. Beside the central nave stands the knotted cross of sacrifice upon which hangs the black Christ:

> He steps in front of it. It is not fear but love that holds him motionless, the same inexplicable love he felt in the stable remembering the morning. Christ's earth-colored face looks down, furrowed with blood. The metal eyes shine beneath the brows of painted torment. The wounded body does not move, though the arms are alive crying pain and welcome. The brief skirt, bordered with jewels, hangs stiff over the belly and down to the knees, and below it descends the lacerated rivers of the legs to their meeting in the single nail that pierces the feet. Jamie is sure that the body of the Savior will not go away, will not escape him as the world did. He kneels. Slowly he opens his pants again and begins to masturbate. The church is silent, there is only the whispering of candles that flicker on both sides of the image. A strange tingling that he has never known before rises from his hot loins. He grips the crucified feet.

> Silence overcomes silence. Something—the wax drippings of the candles—measures time again. The ecstasy of his orgasm passes and he lifts his eyes to the figure and does not know whether his body is Christ's or Christ's is his.

5. Harmony with Experience

Then there is *experience*, which includes all the truth we know through our senses. Orgasm is a unique experience and very much like *The Other*—it is beyond our understanding. It is beyond our describing; we do not have words for it. For all our up-close-and-personal laboratory studies of various sex acts, for all our talk of sex, we can say absolutely nothing meaningfully descriptive or definitive about the *experience* of orgasm. It is metaphysical. It transcends our mortal existence. It is sacred.

We have known that, we humans, for countless thousands of years—which is why, as I've said, the most commonly practiced acts of worship in all history have been sex acts. Yet, fundamentalists today talk of the indecent, depraved, obscene, pornographic.

Fuentes' scene with Jamie in the church continues: The boy lifts the jeweled skirt to discover that the sculpture is a fake. It has no genitals. In fact, it has no thighs or buttocks, just the bare wood of the cross holding the torso and lower legs in place.

There's such irony in this! The Christian Church has rendered impotent for modern humanity the most dynamic object of ecstatic worship in all history: sacrifice of the naked Christ, suffering not in words or wood or porcelain but in heaving, gasping flesh, transubstantiated not through wafers and grape juice and plastic ritual but through bodily passion, the orgasm, the phallus.

The Christian Church has not always been so barren. Leo Steinberg writes in *The Sexuality of Christ in Renaissance Art*, "Renaissance art, both north and south of the Alps, produced a large body of devotional imagery in which the genitalia of the Christ Child, or of the dead Christ, receive such demonstrative emphasis that one must recognize an *ostentation genitalium* (the deliberate showing off of genitals)..." These priceless paintings, many reproduced in Steinberg's book, show the naked penis of Christ, both in infancy and maturity, both flaccid and erect. These artists are portraying Jesus as an erotic, phallic, sexually potent human being, just like us. The phallus was a matter of pride, not shame.

Fundamentalist Christianity has institutionalized psycho-sexual illness and elevated it to a virtue. Sexual shame drove the flagellants to beat themselves bloody, the Skopts of Russia to castrate themselves and slash away their penises. From childhood to old age, sex in our Judeo-Christian society is shrouded in shame, often resulting in a reactionary, artificial hypersexuality that is in itself but another psycho-sexual abnormality.

In contrast to the vast history of humankind, this self-loathing is but a glitch. We who celebrate the self understand the naturalness of phallic worship—of coming to *The Other* in part through our sexuality. Unfortunately, you and I are living during this freakish moment when a noisy but powerful minority would take away our freedom to worship through the phallus and force upon us the sterile, sexless crucifix of Jamie's church.

What are the implications of knowing *The Other* through the phallus? From this perspective, phallic worship—that is, worship not *of* but *through* the phallus—makes sex holy. We open up to it, celebrate it, rather than pursue it in shame.

Erotic magazines and books and videos become sacramental. We have been brainwashed into believing that what evokes lust—what is "pornographic"—is evil. Yet, it is possible to use erotica as some use the Bible—to enrich an act of worship, to set the mood.

As to the phallus, 16th century surgeon Battista Zacchi put it this way: "It has brought forth the Bembos Molzis, the Fortunis, the Franchis, the Varchis, the Ugolin Martinis, the Lorenzo Lenzis, the Dolci, the Titian, the Michelangelos; and after them the Popes, emperors and kings; it has produced the pretty children and the beautiful women and their *sancta sanctorum*, and for this reason we should decree holy days and dedicate vigils and feasts in its honor, not hide it away in scraps of cloth!"

I am well aware that some of you would have rather I ended this book with a final titillating anecdote or stimulating technique, but I would rather end with a challenge. We who celebrate the Bodyspirit have a responsibility to spare those not yet born the sexual shame that some of us have known. We must not sit on the sidelines while boys and girls are being raised in self-loathing, while they are being brainwashed into hating the God of our sacred bodies, while shame replaces celebration.

This is not a battle, as the fundamentalists would have you think, of the moral against the immoral, the decent against the shameful, the family against heathenism. *It is a war of one relatively new religion against another, as old as humankind, the god of the sterile and dead against The Other, the God of the Phallus, and of life and joy. Please join me in taking sides.*

Appendix

When It Comes to Sex
Conditioning Counts

Because I've been writing on health and medical subjects since the mid-1960's, I'm often asked, "Harold, what sort of vitamins and minerals should I be taking to keep my sex life up to snuff?" My answer: "If you're eating a proper diet, rich in zinc, the B complex, vitamins A, E, and calcium, you're probably getting more of the essential nutrients than you need. Taking certain supplements can actually put a strain on your body, and they certainly don't occur in nature in such vast quantities."

I'm not an advocate of extraordinarily large vitamin and mineral supplements.

But I'm a fanatic when it comes to exercise. Why? *Because you can be missing a lung, both legs, both arms, half a liver, twenty feet of intestines and both testicles, and, if you're in the mood for it, still have great sex and orgasms.* That's because, assuming you're getting the necessary intravenous injections, you need just two organs to have great sex: A brain and a penis. (Actually, there are reports that even the penis isn't absolutely necessary; the brain is.)

All organs of the body depend for their efficiency of operation on the oxygen and nutrients they receive. Those nutrients are carried to organ cells through tiny vessels and capillaries—it's through these very narrow corridors that the small cells of the brain and penis receive—or fail to receive—what they need to function at maximum capacity.

The lazy approach has always been to pop a pill, thereby providing those essential nutrients. But the fact is that if those capillaries don't stay opened and the circulation isn't what it ought to be, neither brain nor cock will work to its maximum potential.

Now, this isn't just theory. I have seen men in their fifties write themselves off sexually as over the hill. They flog their penises as though they were dying horses, with nary a resulting whinnie. Then they begin to exercise.

It is as though they are born anew. They feel better, more alert. Their thinking improves. They seem to be awakening from drowsiness. And they feel physically stronger. Their sexual stamina rebounds. They go from a mediocre once-a-week solo sex session to three or four prolonged sexcapades, sometimes with others, each week.

Because I believe your fitness is so important to your sexuality, I'm including here both a fitness test and a compact but complete fitness program. If you choose not to use it— fine. But if you do make up your mind and follow it, within a week you'll notice the difference and within a month you'll thank me.

What is fitness?

When you think of fitness, you may envision a sweat-drenched jogger plodding along a road. Actually, that jogger might be quite unfit, overall, for there are four components to good physical condition.

Cardiorespiratory fitness. The jogger is increasing the strength of his heart and the capacity of his lungs to bring larger quantities of oxygen to the blood. He's also increasing the actual diameter of his blood vessels to improve circulation.

One day he just might get a priceless bonus for his efforts: If a thrombus (blood clot) forms in an artery feeding the heart or brain, that extra diameter (along with the additional blood vessels that exercisers develop) might allow blood to continue flowing to those vital organs and save his life.

Muscular fitness. Physiologists have learned that healthy, fit persons don't begin to lose an appreciable amount of strength until about age seventy, and that endurance remains high well into old age.

Maintaining strength and endurance doesn't require hard work, but it does require *regular* work. Muscles begin to atrophy, or waste away, after less than a week of inactivity. Persons who have an arm or leg in a cast for six weeks or more can usually see the difference in size, compared to the exercised limb.

Flexibility. If you've ever felt that even getting out of bed takes more energy than it used to, that's not your imagination. Chances are you've allowed yourself to become unfit in the flexibility component. Muscles must overcome not only gravity and the weight of the body, but also the resistance of opposing muscles that have grown too short and inelastic.

Coordination, balance, and agility. These fitness factors have their foundation in instinct and their development in learning. Much of what we've learned, however, we can also forget, which is why if we haven't been on a bicycle in twenty years you can still ride one today, but you'd be wobbly. The good news is that you can regain most of what you've lost— quickly—and it will stay with you well into old age.

How fit are you?

If you work at those four physical conditioning components, you will be heading for a point of total fitness. To get there, you must know where you are now. The following tests will reveal your fitness level in each component.

First, though, this caution: About 10 percent of North American men have an undiagnosed heart condition that could be worsened by overexertion. If you have any reason to suspect you're in this group, undergo a medical examination before undertaking the cardiorespiratory test and program. Here are the warning signs:

• High blood pressure, overweight, family history of heart disease, diabetes, high cholesterol, or a tobacco habit

• Dizziness, breathlessness, or chest pains accompanying any physical activity

• A history of heart disease

• Physical inactivity since high school, if you're more than thirty years old.

Cardiorespiratory test. The intent here is to learn what level of exercise will bring your heart rate to 70 percent of its maximum capacity. This is your goal area.

First, determine your personal maximum rate by subtracting your age from 220. If your are forty years old, for example, your maximum is 180 beats per minute (plus or minus ten). Seventy percent of that is 126—or approximately 130 beats per minute.

Now, do any exercise you like at a level that is moderately stressful for you but easy enough that you could maintain it for half an hour. If you're in poor condition, a moderate walk might do. If you're in excellent shape, you might need to jog.

Stop after three minutes. Immediately check your pulse and count the number of beats in fifteen seconds. Multiply it by four. It should equal the 70 percent goal area or slightly higher. (If the rate is 90 percent of your maximum or higher, you are overexerting. There is no benefit in being an over-achiever here.)

Try to remember how you felt when your pulse was in the goal area. You will use that pleasantly strenuous but certainly not exhausting feeling as your guide in your total physical fitness program.

Strength and flexibility. Many schools in the United States and Canada analyze student fitness through the popular Kraus-Weber tests. The ones listed below measure the strength and flexibility of major muscle groups.

1. Lie on your back with your legs straight. Lift your heels ten inches from the floor and hold for ten seconds.

2. Arch your abdomen upward so that you support your weight on your feet and shoulders. Hold for ten seconds.

3. Supporting your weight on your buttocks and lower back, raise both your shoulders and feet from the floor. With legs straight, kick your feet up and down for ten seconds.

4. Lying on your back with shoulders to the floor and legs straight, bring your left leg across the right one and touch the toe to the floor. The leg should be parallel to your outstretched arms. Repeat using the opposite leg.

5. Lie on your side, legs straight, and raise the upper leg at least two feet above the other. Hold for ten seconds.

6. Lie on your stomach and, without bending your knees, lift your feet ten inches from the floor. Hold for ten seconds.

7. In the same position, lift your head and upper chest ten inches from the floor and hold for ten seconds.

8. With knees slightly bent, do a half sit-up (halfway to a sitting position) and hold for ten seconds.

9. With your weight on your buttocks, raise your legs (keeping them straight) and your back so that your body forms a "V." Hold for ten seconds.

The Kraus-Weber tests indicate the *minimum* level of fitness that school systems deem acceptable—ideally, you should have more strength and flexibility than those tests require. You should, for example, be able to do at least ten push-ups, ten sit-ups, ten chin-ups, and, sitting with your knees slightly bent, touch your forehead to your knees.

In doing these tests, don't continue to strain if a tight muscle is causing pain. Instead, include flexibility exercises of the type you need in your fitness program.

Balance, coordination, and agility. Stand on one foot for thirty seconds. You may use arm movement to maintain balance, but if you hop you fail.

Skip a rope fifteen times in succession. Although children do it all the time, it actually requires a good deal of both coordination and agility. Without both, you won't get past the second jump in a row.

How to get fit

Once you have completed these tests and determined your level of fitness, you can begin your own personal fitness program, which is broken into three phases.

The cardiorespiratory phase. An effective program that will give you a stronger heart, healthier circulation, and greater oxygen-processing capacity must meet four standards: It must be long enough, intense enough, frequent enough, and pleasant enough to keep you motivated.

Ideally, you should do cardiorespiratory exercises every other day—and certainly not miss more than three days in succession. After that, your body begins to lose the conditioning you've already achieved. After ten weeks of inactivity you'll be back where you started.

Unless you're training all-out—and that's not fun for most of us—you'll need to keep your heart rate at the goal area for at least twenty minutes. It's virtually impossible to take your pulse while exercising, so familiarize yourself with the sensation of exercising in the goal area by stopping and taking your pulse frequently on the first day.

Probably by the end of your first week you will discover this: Although on the first day you might have reached the goal area with a brisk walk, by the second week, you'll have to begin jogging to get there. Yet you won't feel any more stress than you did walking the week before.

Why? Your heart has already grown stronger. Your blood vessels are enlarging and new ones are branching out to the vital organs. You're using oxygen more efficiently. Your fitness will continue to improve dramatically but never so much as in these first weeks when you need the encouragement most.

As important as these factors are, choosing an activity that you can enjoy is every bit as essential. Nothing will be gained if you quit after two weeks because you're bored.

One of the most popular cardiorespiratory exercises is jogging, with 31 million adherents in the US alone. It's inexpensive, relatively convenient except in rain or snow, and it's not too difficult to find another jogger to keep you company. But some people simply don't like jogging.

Alternatives abound. One of the best is swimming. Not only does it improve cardiorespiratory fitness, but it comes as close as anything to the perfect exercise. It builds strength in most of the major muscle groups and enhances flexibility and coordination. If you enjoy swimming, try to find a year-round swimming facility nearby. Otherwise you might be tempted to abandon the program when winter gives you an excuse.

Sports are another alternative, but it must be the right sport. Golf, especially the motorized-cart variety, is of virtually no benefit to the cardiovascular system. Nor is football, unless you're a wide receiver and your team plays a nonstop passing game. But twenty minutes of racquetball or tennis three times a week is all the conditioning you'll ever need if you can keep a volley going long enough to work up a sweat.

In fact, if you enjoy it, twenty minutes of calisthenics three times a week will give you every component of fitness, and you can exercise anywhere—even in a hotel room—regardless of the weather. And you don't have to dress for it. The insurmountable drawback for most people is that they find calisthenics incredibly boring.

For many of us, the solution is to join a health club, where we can meet others who are also following a fitness program. Companionship during exercise acts as a motivator, as does the subtle pressure not to be the first to quit the program. If you go this route, be sure to exercise with someone whose fitness level is similar to yours. Otherwise, one of you might have to perform below the goal area in order not to exhaust the other.

Still another excellent total fitness activity is modern aerobic dance. It provides—in addition to cardiorespiratory conditioning—flexibility, strength, balance, coordination, and agility conditioning. Many professional football players take part in aerobic dancing.

Strength and flexibility phase. If you choose swimming, calisthenics, or dance for your cardiorespiratory program, you'll be gaining flexibility and strength as well. Otherwise, you can regain flexibility through a routine as brief as five minutes, every third day. Simply practice the exercises described in the strength and flexibility test.

Avoid bobbing or jerking motions when attempting these moves. If you're sitting on the floor and lowering your forehead to your knees, for example, stop when the hamstring muscles of your thighs and those in your back and neck register moderate discomfort. Simply hold that position. Forcing the muscle to stretch might well have the opposite result—it might go into a protective reflex spasm (a cramp) or, worse, actually tear.

After about twenty seconds of maintaining the same position, you'll feel the muscle tension ease and, like a minor miracle, you'll be able to lower your head a few more inches. Slowly. Stop again before you suffer more than minor discomfort. That's enough for one day. At the next flexibility session you'll progress from where you left off.

The Kraus-Weber tests, remember, are for minimum fitness. To achieve good conditioning strength, extend the holds to thirty seconds, the sit-ups to forty, and push-ups to fifteen. Beyond that, you're on your way to excellence.

Balance, coordination, and agility phase. If you plan a routine designed specifically to enhance these components of fitness, as little as half-an-hour once a week will serve the purpose. You can build an effective workout in these areas around a bicycle, jump rope, trampoline, or balance beam.

All forms of gymnastics draw upon balance, coordination, and agility, and if you're interested, there are adult gymnastic classes.

Again, if you are committed to a total fitness activity—swimming, calisthenics, or dance—you need not include this phase in a fitness program. Otherwise, schedule one fifteen-minute session a week.

If you choose a total fitness exercise, try to work out every other day, or every third day at the least. If you decide on jogging, follow the same schedule but intersperse three days of strength and flexibility exercises.

There's no advantage in two consecutive days of cardiorespiratory training—your body needs a "day off" to increase heart muscle strength. The same is true of other muscles.

The following is a sample fitness schedule:

Day one: cardiorespiratory phase, jogging (twenty minutes)

Day two: strength and flexibility, calisthenics (fifteen minutes)

Day three: cardiorespiratory phase, square dancing (twenty minutes)

Day four: strength and flexibility, Kraus-Weber test (five minutes)

Day five: cardiorespiratory phase, tennis (twenty minutes)

Day six: strength and flexibility, swimming (twenty minutes)

Day seven: balance, coordination, and agility, slow bicycle ride (fifteen minutes).

The schedule need never be boring. After a week or two, you'll begin to *think* fitness, and you'll find yourself seeking other forms of exercise. If you'd rather play tennis than jog one day, go ahead. And if you think a run in the park might be more fun than swimming, follow the impulse.

Soon you'll find yourself looking forward to being active. That day you'll find you have the sex drive and capacity of a man twenty years younger.

RECORD YOUR EXPERIENCES ON THE FOLLOWING PAGE